THE 4TH BOMB

Inside London's Terror Storm

Daniel Obachike

FLORAN BOOKS

Floran Books

www.floranpublishing.co.uk
Published by Floran

ISBN: 978-0-9555363-0-4

Dedicated to

Christian Njoya Diawara Small

and the victims of the 7/7 attacks

Contents

I

*Law is the process by which the unmanifest
becomes the manifest;
It's the process by which
the observer becomes the observed.*

~Chapter 1~

Hurrah!

It started in Africa, the place from where all humanity and spirituality came rolling out across the continents, to the East and to the West.

The timeless narrative repeated itself once more with the Live 8 concerts. They were billed as the final push to make poverty in Africa history in the run-up to the G8 summit in Gleneagles that the leaders of the world's largest economies would attend later that week.

And what a show it was. A smiling Tony Blair received the adulation of the masses for his saintly words, pledging to save Africa from poverty, AIDS and other plagues.

Sir Bob banged the drum while Bono played second fiddle.

The material girl's interest in Africa also came to the fore. Onstage, the former star was shadowed by a former starving African child who since the 80's concert's had grown into a perfect picture of health.

Thank Bob, the audience thought collectively, as a smattering of Africans looked on among a sea of euphoric faces.

Sweet Pete stumbled shambolic style against the piano as Sir Elton trooped belligerently onwards, his fingers falling up and down along the piano keys. The show must drag on, and drag on it did, until Ricky Gervais summed up the mood precisely.

'Are you avin' a laugh? He asked the crowd.

Regardless of whether he actually meant it, the crowd duly obliged. He responded by chuckling at the madness of it all, before leaving them with a glimpse of his King Tut dance moves, resurrected from an eighties dance craze.

1

Daniel returned, switching on the TV later that evening in time to see the concert's finale. *The Who* performed a rousing set of their old hits. And that was it. *Nostalgia*.

The masses went home contented and despite rumblings of trouble ahead Britain was *Great* again, if just for a moment.

Poverty? That was history!

Trouble? That was in a far away land covered by sand.

There was a definite fizz and excited expectancy in the air.

~Chapter 2~

Looks & Observations

A sudden jolt caught many standing passengers off guard.

The train shuddered noisily onwards for a moment, drawing a few concerned expressions until a voice crackled in over the P.A system.

To most the driver's explanation was barely audible amid the early morning crush but his unperturbed east-end tone must have been reassuring, as after a brief period of murmuring the passengers attention returned to their books, newspapers and Mp3 players and the train continued on its path unhindered.

Daniel added 'temporary electrical defect in the Kings Cross area' to a long list of excuses London's transport network was renown for; wondering if the driver's cockney accent would be as reassuring if they'd been travelling at a higher altitude of say… 35,000 feet?

Casting this thought aside he took a firmer grip of an overhead handrail and stared blankly out of the window. Through it he watched the familiar landscape flying by, transforming from the greying tower blocks, apartments and industrial estates into the gleaming glass and steel structures of the city looming large on the horizon, glinting in the morning sun.

The day had gotten off to an okay start. He woke up sometime before the insistent buzz of the radio alarm clock sounded but now found he was running slightly late.

Hurriedly he plugged the iron into the wall socket and as soon as a small red light indicated its readiness, he began ironing in firm sweeping motions back and forth.

'Bloody shirt' he muttered under his breath, trying to flatten a particularly resistant crease for what seemed like the umpteenth time. Time was pressing on. He began to think his decision to steam iron the shirt for that added look of efficiency might prove to be less than efficient time-wise.

Still, a crisply pressed shirt was something he could appreciate, especially on days like this, days when the sunshine made the extra effort worthwhile. Because who knew, with drinks after work in mind, maybe he would draw the odd glance from a suitably effected female or two? So he pressed on, absorbed in his task, preparing himself for the day ahead in a silence punctuated only by the gentle hiss and whoosh from the iron as plumes of steam evaporated upwards from its nozzles.

~

He wore the pale grey shirt without a tie, a look he agreed was efficient yet relaxed.

In the bathroom he slipped a belt through the loops of his dark grey trousers and stood for a moment surveying the fruits of his labour in the mirror with a mild look of satisfaction.

The look quickly deserted him when it suddenly struck him.

He'd forgotten to keep an eye on the time. It was nearly 8.25. Any chance of catching the 8:27 Enfield Town to Liverpool Street station had gone and with it went any possibility of reaching work on time.

'Damn' he muttered. He'd managed it everyday this week so far and would miss the puerile sense of supremacy it afforded him each morning when his petulant project manager came a-hovering moments after 9 O'clock.

Picking up the pace he skipped downstairs, gathered some folders off a cabinet in the bedroom and stuffed them into a small black gym-sack.

'Wallet, keys, mobile phone... and sunglasses' he murmured, re-enforcing each item with a verbal check before slinging the bag over his shoulder.

He left his apartment and went down the hallway to the lifts. When the lift reached the ground floor he exited and walked past the security manager whose head momentarily glanced up from between the pages of a copy of The Daily Star.

He paused at the top of the stairs outside the apartment block to put on a pair of Dolce & Gabbana shades then sauntered down the steps, off to Enfield Town train station.

Twelve minutes later Daniel stood aboard the train ready to depart for Liverpool Street and before long it was speeding along the rails towards its destination.

Maybe it was an upbeat mood brought on by the sunshine that caused a change of plan. He decided against travelling to work via Liverpool Street with the grey brigade despite his matching monochrome attire; instead he took a more colourful route to work, getting off the train halfway at Seven Sisters station. From there he would get an underground tube train to his office at Old Street.

Turning the corner out of Seven Sisters train station he leisurely strolled the short distance past the faded fly posters, shabby off licenses and kebab shops basking in the warm rays as he stepped among the steady stream of people heading for the underground at the end of the road. Behind his shades his pupils flitted to and fro, assessing, quantifying and classifying the array of females of assorted shades on their way to work dressed in neat business suits, figure hugging denim and floral summery dresses complete with strappy open-toed heels.

The already favourable ratio of women of colour on this route reached a crescendo during the morning rush hour, making what was a fine vantage point, fabulous in weather this good as he knew only too well. For the junction of Seven Sisters and the High Road was a hub of humanity.

It was a place where African, Caribbean and latterly South American communities collided in a kaleidoscope of colour.

Transient tourists and city commuters jostled briefly among the revelry before racing down the steps into the underground, leaving crowds behind at street level to besiege approaching double-deckers and bendy-buses in large packs.

As he descended the subways stairs Daniel's shades came off. He joined those funnelling through its passageways into the station. The jostling its thoroughfare afforded reminded him that time was at a premium. Time equalled money.

In the busy ticket hall people accelerated, brushing past like automatons on missions with deadlines and destinations.

Amid the rush he became aware of the eyes of a young woman following him. Her gaze lingered a tad beyond the time in which the look might have been considered just a cursory one.

Something told him his change of travel plans must have been inspired, as he scanned her discreetly.

With a flutter of her eyelashes she averted her gaze and passed through a ticket barrier. This caused Daniel's leisurely amble to develop a sense of priority.

Obeying a primordial instinct he sidestepped the commuters zig-zagging in front of him. From his back pocket he produced a travelcard and in one fluid movement darted through the barrier, catching a glimpse of his quarry as she disappeared down the escalator. As the rumble of an approaching train grew louder he strode briskly down after her.

Her mauve and cream checked skirt produced a flourish that eased into a gentle sashay when her plum-coloured leather boots stepped off at the bottom and she made her way along the platform. As the train pulled in he followed her onboard and took the seat beside her.

Moments later the tube's doors slid shut.

Only then, did he begin to think of what to say.

Would he play it confident but polite, or humorous and cocky?

The tube train squealed into motion. As it accelerated his mind raced, searching for the right manner in which to make her acquaintance. Now the tricky part, he thought. Adopting the right approach after their initial exchange of eye contact had to be done sensitively taking into account their surroundings.

This was due to any self-respecting female's *in-built* resistance and experience had shown him that this resistance was particularly toughened when it came to African and Caribbean females.

It was a resistance they built-up through adolescence, honed combating the unwanted attention of males, whose African free-spiritedness sometimes led them to believe they had the right to liberally hail down women in the street like some form of unregulated taxi service. This was a category Daniel clearly wished to avoid, but he soon found it wasn't long before contact was made.

As the accelerating trains motion became more pronounced, her thigh began to brush, ever so lightly against his.

At one point she almost seemed to be cajoling him to action, but his vision remained fixed straight-ahead as though he were impervious to the friction generated by their proximity.

This energy must have been palpable to the middle-aged lady sitting opposite them, who peered up from her magazine and smiled knowingly at him. The sheepish smile Daniel returned barely concealed his embarrassment.

When he glanced up a second time the lady's smile had broadened to a grin. With no newspaper on hand to block her intrusive gaze he stared downwards and hoped the lady would mind her own business or get off, but it was the focus of his unspoken intentions who clasped her bag to her shoulder in readiness to disembark.

Any high hopes he'd had began sinking fast.

Damn! He thought, equally disgusted by his own inaction and the prying lady opposite.

The day that started so brightly and full of promise petered out as the young women stood up and got off.

Daniel remained in his seat, *in his place* and there he sat, feeling impotent, seemingly hindered by an archaic British commandment. *Thou commuters shall remain mute.*

It was as if *some thing*, not some one, had interfered. Something with the power to affect the fate of those subjugated by it. Regardless of culture, ethnicity or religion, these beliefs had been imposed the moment the train doors slid shut.

He stole a wistful glance as the object of his undeclared intent melted into the crowded platform. As the tube drew away from Finsbury Park he sighed discontentedly, tussling with the strange force that had inhibited him rendering him powerless.

It was a misguided loyalty stemming from a belief, a belief in an alien etiquette distilled from deep-seated Victorian values that was manipulating him and the other passengers as they sat aboard a Victoria line train that shot through London's blue vein, heading for its heart.

The lady opposites look seemed to have taken on the proportions of a glare, observing him like an item of curiosity or an obscure tribal custom that a colonial anthropologist might take delight in quantifying or classifying.

Maybe she twigged this sentiment as she scurried back to her Hello magazine to apply the same *stare and compare* values to the glossy world of suffering celebs, leaving Daniel to dwell momentarily on the flutter of an eye-lid, the sumptuous fullness of the lips and a brush of the thigh that was in touching distance yet seemingly out of reach.

A few stops later his shredded bliss was interrupted by an announcement that issued from the train's PA system.

'Due to an earlier incident, Kings Cross underground station has been closed… until further notice'.

The message was greeted with the kind of sighs and groans that normally accompany a poor joke being reeled off for the umpteenth time.

Eyes rolled towards the heavens as frustrated passengers were given further evidence of London's inept transport system.

'*Passengers are advised to continue their journey seeking alternative connections to destinations*' came the advice.

Necks strained up at tube maps. Lumbering brains still in their pre-caffeinated period grudgingly ground into gear, calculating the extra-time hastily revised routes would add.

Having already begun easing into 'accentuate the positive' mode Daniel took the morning's second minor setback in his stride. A glance at his watch told him it was a few minutes before 9 O'clock. By his estimation, reaching work by 9:30 would be good going under present circumstances.

The train reduced its speed passing through Kings Cross's empty platform and accelerated onwards in a hushed silence.

Strangely this didn't strike any passengers as unusual, even though it was the height of the rush hour and not a single soul or transport employee was in evidence on the platform.

At Euston, the next station, its doors slid open allowing passengers to disembark. Some did, but after a short interval the train remained on the platform with its doors still open.

Soon passengers began exchanging quizzical looks having failed to understand any of the garbled messages issuing from the train's tinny sounding P.A system.

Small games of Chinese whispers broke out in its carriages. Occupants who mouthed 'what did he say?' to fellow passengers were largely met with shrugs as no information or indication when the tube would move came forth.

After waiting a further 5 minutes the passenger's frustrations began to tell.

Soon they began leaving its carriages, peeling off in dribs and drabs until finally the driver's announcement came confirming the train's withdrawal from service.

With that his relevance was severed mid-utterance and the trickle became a flood, as passengers deserted the stranded train in droves.

Daniel joined the exodus in search of the fabled *alternative connection*. Unsure of exactly where it was, he too fell victim like many to a highly contagious airborne virus known as 'herd mentality' that seemed to be breaking out all around.

He pushed past an indignant suit, extolling the virtues of the Parisian transport system to a colleague in light of the award of the 2012 Olympics to Britain the previous day and joined the procession trudging towards the escalators.

They found that transport staff had switched off the escalators. No doubt to prevent the multitude from streaming out en-mass in panic-stricken scenes reminiscent of a 50's disaster movie.

The tactic worked, though the orderly manner of the evacuation was probably due to most commuters thinking it was just another small sign of London's decadent decay, no different to the ones regularly served up in daily digestible amounts, another sign of a capital spluttering, throttled by its own ideology.

As Daniel neared the escalator's summit, the tone of proceedings changed again.

An announcement boomed from the station's tannoys, calling for the *entire* station to be evacuated due to a *security alert*.

Well, at least now he had an excuse sufficient to pacify even the most despotic of bosses, he thought.

He followed the throngs that merged, swelling up from the Victoria and Northern line branches onto Euston's main foyer dragging his heels with all the haste reserved for the annual office fire drill.

Many commuters headed straight for Euston station's exit, seeking alternative routes, the rest crowded the main foyer staring up at train departure boards with mobiles clasped against their ears attempting to contact their offices but the mobile networks seemed to be down, judging by the length of queues seen at a number of telephone kiosks.

9:06 AM

Daniel wandered through the foyer and stepped outside into the warm sunlight.

He was still trying to get his bearings so for a moment or two stood surveying his surroundings unsure which of the bus queues to join.

To his left suited city professionals swelled the taxi ranks leaving city workers and tourists alike to besiege the few transport staff on hand offering hapless commuters advice.

He watched them turn and head to one of the bus stops to jostle in the impossibly overcrowded queues.

The scenes around him mirrored those he'd seen at Seven Sisters earlier, except the rhythmic radiance had been replaced with a less convivial, more frenetic edge, reflective of Euston's grey concrete.

As he stood there a stocky built young African man headed across from the foyer exit.

What made him noticeable to Daniel was the mischievous smirk on his face as he bowled past. It was as though he was privy to some banter or joke that Daniel had yet to twig.

His look was a cursory one, a non-hostile yet competitive glance. Comparing like with like perhaps, which Daniel took as being more a look of recognition.

The man continued heading towards the bus stops while Daniel stood trying to work out a route from Euston station to his office.

He was still plotting when a familiar face strode out of Euston Station's main foyer.

It was the face of a man whose demeanour was one of a calm focused determination, a face Daniel recognised immediately.

It was the face of his friend Christian Njoya Diawara Small.

Just the week before Christian and himself had been hanging out with another friend of theirs, Brian.

Brian had roped them into trying their hand at Salsa dancing at the Ion Bar, a club in Ladbroke Grove, near Notting Hill.

Christian smiled, exchanging a nod of recognition as he strode by looking smart in a blue and white shirt and a tie that complimented his smart grey suit.

Daniel nodded back, acknowledging his friend's inability to stop and chat and he watched Christian head off towards Euston's bus terminal merging into a crowd of commuters milling around the bus stops ahead.

9:17 AM

There'd been no sign of any buses entering the terminal since he'd ventured out of the station 15 minutes before.

Daniel was sure the first of many probing emails must have been fired in the direction of his inbox by now.

The E.T.A of 9:30 now looked hopelessly optimistic.

He looked upwards at the sun trying to warm his face on a small ray trying to poke out through an overcast patch of greyish sky, then ambled over to one of the bus stops.

There, a mixed-raced girl in a red outfit spoke loudly into her mobile phone providing live commentary of her transport tribulations for all those conversant in scouse.

She reminded him he needed to stop wondering and find out exactly how he was going to reach work. After drifting towards the front of an evolving mass of commuters he scanned the bus stop's route information and timetables.

The manoeuvre left him none the wiser, but allowed him to move towards the front of the bulbous queue, a position from where he stood a better chance of pouncing on a bus ahead of the clamouring pack.

9:23 AM

'At last!' he said as a bus appeared on the horizon and swung into the terminal. The number 205 bus caused quite a stir.

With crowding almost at biblical proportions it was definitely a case of board now, ask questions later, unless passengers were prepared to wait another half hour.

Daniel's position ensured he was one of the first to hop aboard.

'Does this bus go to Old Street?' he asked, rummaging through his bag for his travelcard.

'Or to Angel?' he added hopefully. The driver shook his head.

'Nomba tutty... dat bus stop' came the reply in a heavy African accent. The driver nodded towards the bus stop ahead.

'This is turning out to be a nightmare!' Daniel stropped, wading through the mass of passengers behind him to join a large queue at the bus stop in front.

The scrum to board the 205 had signalled to anyone still unaware that the battle lines had been drawn.

The office-bound, sensing the transport problem had tipped into a near crisis, eyed their number anxiously and an undeclared fight to reach the bastions of commerce commenced. Daniel joined the queue gradually becoming more accepting of his predicament. Maybe he had himself to blame.

If he'd left home on time or stayed on the train to Liverpool Street he wouldn't still be here.

A minute later, just when he'd resigned himself to the prospect of an arduous wait, another bus trundled into view.

Even before the crowd were able to make out its number the queue began jostling with expectancy. It was a number 30.

They began drifting like marathon runners before a starter's gun, a wavering bulge collectively trying to anticipate the precise spot it would stop.

With a hiss its doors swung open and the bus jolted to a halt.
One of the first aboard was Daniel, waving his travelcard.
'Does this bus go to Old Street?' he asked the driver.
The bus driver looked up at him.
'… No' came the halting, almost stuttered response.
The hesitant response was at odds with the advice his African colleague had provided minutes earlier.
Eye contact ensued as both men's glares wrestled momentarily until the driver turned glibly away staring dead ahead.
Daniel concealed his circumspect and stood aside allowing those in the bottleneck forming behind him to shove past.
As more passengers flashed their passes and boarded, he deliberated. Which driver should he believe? More pertinent was *why* would this driver give him contradicting advice?

'Are you goin' near Kings Cross, mate?' said a commuter.
'I need to get to Angel…' a woman asked.
'Does this bus go to Holborn?' inquired another.
Almost every one of the displaced commuters boarding the bus had a question for the driver.
After evaluating a number of the driver's grunted responses to these questions, Daniel opted to stay onboard, on the rationale that it was heading in the general direction of Angel.
Angel wasn't far from Old Street so it was a safer bet than remaining stranded at Euston for an unspecified period.
He moved further down the rapidly filling bus and stood by the bus's central exit doors, just in case the driver wasn't lying and he needed to make a quick exit.

09:31 AM

Finally it pulled out of Euston's bus terminus fully laden.

Like most of the passengers who'd managed to board, Daniel thought the ordeal that was reaching work in London would soon be over for another day, but a few minutes after exiting the bus terminal the premature nature of this assumption became apparent.

The bus had travelled a distance of approximately 150 metres.

It was crawling at a snail's pace, taking what seemed like an age stuck in the Euston Road.

There was a fair amount of traffic congestion in the vicinity, the type normally expected in central London during the height of the rush hour, but the number 30's progress or lack of it went way beyond this.

Daniel huffed as the bus came to a complete standstill.

The street was abuzz with activity, but traffic was going nowhere fast. A helicopter whirred by overhead as police sirens wailed intermittently in the distance.

Traffic was beginning to grind to a complete halt.

White vans sought detours and black cabs that had descended on the area eager to make a quick killing off stranded commuters found themselves caught in the quagmire.

9:37AM

After 4 minutes at a total standstill Daniel's ire began to rise.

If only he'd stayed on the Liverpool Street train that morning.

If only he'd stayed on the 205 bus, which he imagined was halfway to its destination by now. Daniel marched up to the front of the bus determined to find out the cause of the hold-up and peered out of its front window.

Through it he saw a navy metallic blue BMW 5-Series straddled across the bus's path, blocking its route down Euston Road towards King's Cross.

He was even more puzzled by what he saw to the right of it.

There, a second car, a black Mercedes estate was blocking it from the direction of Upper Woburn Place at an absurd angle in the road. The two cars formed an L-shaped blockade.

All this was while the bus driver sat impassively in his cab.

After a further minute of this stalemate a police motorcycle whizzed up sounding a burst of its siren, arriving to find out what was causing the hold-up.

'At last!' muttered Daniel relieved to see the police motorcyclist speaking to the driver of the BMW.

After a brief exchange the policeman suddenly revved up his motorcycle's pedal, turned and sped away. The two dark cars however, remained in position. Their blockade continued for another two minutes till the driver of the BMW suddenly performed a quick manoeuvre in the road and sped off.

The bus driver revved the bus's engine and disengaged the brakes. The bus crept forward. The Mercedes moved out of the way and left the scene allowing the bus to turn right, diverted into Upper Woburn Place. The reason for the variation to the number 30 bus's normal route was unclear, as no temporary diversion signs of any sort were in evidence.

9:42ᴀᴍ

After an initial burst of speed the bus slowed back down to a
slow crawl, stopping and starting it ways along.
One minute later the bus's middle doors were suddenly flung
open in front of him. Daniel looked around nonplussed.
The driver had taken the unusual step of opening the bus's
central exit doors *right* on the corner of Upper Woburn Place
when nobody had rung the bell.
What the hell is he doing? Daniel wondered, noticing that he'd
kept the bus's front doors shut, preventing two passers-by
from boarding. Daniel watched him wave them away when
one of them tapped on the entrance door.
Through the bus's front window he could see the only bus stop
at the far end of Tavistock Square, some 90 metres away.
Bemused and frustrated, Daniel scratched his head.
Some passengers on the lower deck had also had enough of the
painstaking progress and with the doors now open, seized the
opportunity to disembark.
When others on the upper deck noticed a few leaving the bus
and heading off towards Kings Cross they followed likewise.
The clomping of feet was heard as more and more passengers
came down the stairs, off the bus and began making their way
down the street. Daniel had to move from where he'd stood
resolutely by the right of the exit doors out of the way of
leaving passengers. This lasted a good few minutes, as more of
them realised Kings Cross was less than a 15-minute walk
away.
The rush to disembark had subsided by the time the sound of a
pair of dainty high-heels click-clacking their way down the
stairs drew his attention.

He turned round to see petit brunette in a brown business suit standing beside him.

She swept a flick of hair behind her ear as she hovered by the doorway and threw a hesitant glance in Daniel's direction.

Her indecision seemed to be preventing the driver from closing the doors and continuing the bus's journey.

'Where is it you wanna go?' Daniel offered, seeing her predicament.

Her look of uncertainty formed an expectant smile.

She uttered the name of a place.

'Er, that's in North London', he replied, wondering why a young white male in a grey shower-proof top who'd come downstairs now sat beside the open doors watching him advise her.

Probably a lost tourist, Daniel thought, noting the man's attire and dark grey rucksack.

'Is that near King's Cross?' the brunette asked.

'No, not really', Daniel replied.

'Get off here and follow those people' he said, gesturing ahead while wondering why the man was trying to avoid eye contact. It seemed odd behaviour for a lost tourist.

The brunette's dainty heels were clacking their way down the street in the direction he motioned. She would have been the last passenger to get off before the bus doors swished shut, but just before they did, the man that sat by the door leapt up and darted out.

He was the last person to disembark before the bus set off.

9:46AM

The bus lurched forward then settled back into a familiar pattern of stops and starts, inching it's way towards Tavistock Square. It was half empty now with only Daniel, the bus driver and a handful of people seated towards the rear remaining on its lower deck. Daniel glanced at his watch restlessly.

He was more than slightly peeved. He'd been stuck in Euston for 45 minutes. Still, he stood resolutely in the space on the bus usually reserved for babies' buggies.

As the bus came to yet another standstill, a deep sigh couldn't ease the simmering frustration he felt as pedestrians ploughed past, leaving the bus trailing in their wake.

He placed the small gymsack he was holding over his shoulders and grabbed the overhead handrail above.

Then he heard a cockney accent that sounded more Eastern European than East end.

It was calling out from the bus driver's cab across the street.

'Ey, scuse mi mate… woss the name of this road?'

'Huh?' Daniel gasped, completely failing to reconcile the logic of a bus driver that asked *passers-by* for directions.

'Woss the name of this road?' repeated the driver.

The response to his question was a loud deep boom, instantly recognisable as a bomb blast. It made the entire bus jar violently as a shockwave tore through it. Bits of window frame and rubber strips rained down as he fell forward.

Why me? A distant voice asked. The strange force engulfed him, sending him sprawling forward through the air.

Time yawned. Many things entered his consciousness in that moment. Out of the corner of his eye thousands of disintegrated glass fragments glinted as they caught a shaft of light, glistening for a moment before falling like fading stars as gravity intervened.

20

His hands and knees bore the brunt of the impact becoming encrusted with shattered glass as he embraced the floor.

His face contorted into a grimace and pressed down, as low as was humanly possible. There he remained till the roar had given way to an eerie silence.

Seconds after he tentatively opened an eye and lifted his head a fraction. To his right he heard the sound of clambering steps.

The bus driver had got off and was murmuring Hail Mary's on seeing what had become of his bus.

Daniel lifted his head and peeked over to his left to where the blast seemed to have emanated. The back of the bus had taken on a completely different form. It was now shrouded in a darkness permeated by three pairs of eyes that stared out at him, all with the same look of fear and incredulity.

Three females were huddled, writhing together on the bus's floor each trying to slide beneath the other for safety. Their mouths were aghast with silent inhaled screams. They glared at him as if imploring him to provide them with some kind of explanation. The eerie silence that descended began to fill with the sound of their faint whimpers escalating in tandem with their rising sense of dread.

Keeping his chin pressed to the floor Daniel crawled forward and peered cautiously through a gap in the bus's centre doors that was now jutting awkwardly outwards.

Scattered amongst tangled pieces of metal, plastic and splintered bus parts, he could make out what looked like a discarded body lying motionless in a crumpled heap in the gutter. Even as this horrifying realisation ingrained itself in the recesses of his mind, somehow the terror still seemed distant.

His mind raced through a course of strategies on a tidal wave of energy surging through him. This energy was overriding his emotions and would influence his actions.

Crawling over to his right through the sea of shattered glass, he reached the bus's front door. It was slightly ajar from when the driver left allowing a narrow view outside.

Through it he could make out some black railings, a doorway, *cover*, not more than 25 metres away.

Daniel wavered momentarily as some grim variables passed fleetingly through his mind. A secondary device, a black man running away from the scene of a bomb, the crack of a marksman's shot. He used the moment's hesitance to summon up a deep breath and 12 seconds after the explosion had determined a course of action.

Fragments of glass showered everywhere as he leapt up and out of the bus, through the thin smoky haze that gently dispersed upwards from the twisted wreck.

~Chapter 3~

Angels & Agents

He hit the ground running and veered sharply right along Tavistock Square leaving the death strewn in his wake.

The crunch of shattered glass being pulverised underfoot pounded a sizzling metronome that drowned out all else.

In those precious few seconds he put as much distance between himself and the carnage running 20, 30 meters and more towards the doorway and beyond. Only then did he dare lift his gaze to see what lay ahead.

'What the...?' he gasped in disbelief, spitting a string of expletives as he came skidding to a halt.

Up ahead he saw a man dressed in an all black uniform, advancing, pointing something at him from chest height.

He could hardly believe his eyes; the man in black was *filming*, filming the death and carnage with a black camcorder, a matter of seconds after the explosion.

As Daniel's eyes met the camera's lens the man suddenly veered wildly, turning the direction the camera was focused away from the stricken bus towards the green.

Beyond the cameraman stood a line of uniformed police behind a POLICE - DO NOT CROSS cordon that one of them was extending from the railings on the corner of the road across to the green of Tavistock Square.

Daniel spun round, silently beseeching anyone present to answer any of the questions colliding in his head.

That was the moment he clapped eyes on an even more unbelievable sight. That was when he caught sight of the bus.

It was a sight that bypassed logic completely. He caught the tail end of the bus's roof completing a slow motion pirouette in the air as it floated gently to earth.

It settled in a crumpled heap in the road between hastily discarded vehicles.

Daniel shrugged, totally dumbfounded by all he saw.

The horror was tempered by the odd fact that he could see signs of life amid the carnage. A group of people milled about at the front of the now roofless upper deck.

He stared at it with apathy, still seething at the absurdity of the bus driver's moronic questioning, somehow deeming the situation he found himself in attributable to him.

From behind he could hear a man's voice wailing in agony further down the street near to where the bus stop was.

It was a surreal scene. Before he knew it a group of men with rucksacks had sprung from nowhere and begun pulling bodies from the wreckage. They carried out their task with workman-like detachment, while medical staff that ventured out from the British Medical Association building on hearing the bang stood aghast in total shock and awe at what had occurred on their doorstep. Daniel cast an eye across the road.

He noticed a young man wearing a florescent yellow bib standing on the grass of Tavistock Green.

The man stood impassively while those who'd been near the bus ran for their lives in panic and those who heard the bang from further afield turned around trying to fathom what the horrendous noise was. Daniel crossed over to remonstrate.

'What's happening, what's goin' on?' he growled. The young man didn't flinch in the face of his flailing gesticulations.

'Wait over there… on the grass' came the reply.

This was the man's paltry response, answering as though he'd spent the last 3 months *rehearsing* that single line.

Daniel looked across.

He could see a triage point seemed to have already taken shape on the grass in the direction the man motioned, but not in the mood for an impromptu picnic on the meditative surrounds of the Square the young man's directions fell on defiant ears.

Daniel stormed back across the road to where the medical staff were now trying to decide which of the horrendously wounded victims lying on the square to assist first.

Something had aroused Daniel's suspicions about a man in a grey suit wailing loudly and rolling on the ground by railings 70 metres away from the bus.

He was at a loss to explain how the man already had a bandage applied to his head *seconds* after the bomb blast.

Closer inspection revealed the man's trousers had a neat tear along the seam of one leg up to the knee.

Surely none of his injuries were caused by the bus explosion? Daniel thought, returning his attention to those less vocal and more in need of assistance nearer the bus.

He saw a woman sitting alone on the steps of a building 20 meters from the wreckage. She was quivering uncontrollably.

Daniel realised he must have ran straight past her moments before. Her hands were clasped around the sides of her head and her eyes fixed his with a mournful stare.

As he drew closer he noticed the neat dappled effect splattered droplets of blood had made all over her white leather coat.

He thought their delicate arrangement was strangely uniform and pretty for something so grisly and chaotic, somehow managing to compartmentalise this most graphic of designs from the murderous handiwork of its artistes.

He sat down on the step beside her and placed an arm around her shoulder in an attempt to comfort her and there they sat.

For the second time that morning Daniel searched for something to say but his mind was blank.

What was there *to* say? The woman's face bore the same distant stare. Daniel looked at her then back at the increased activity in the square.

'Don't worry... its okay' he blurted, after a stony silence.

As soon as the utterance came forth he realised its absurdity.

Okay? It was not okay. *Deal with reality*, a voice urged him, a bomb had gone off! It was serious and there were a number of other things concerning him about the picture in front of him.

The woman quivered slightly and remained silent.

Any attempt at small talk was a futile endeavor.

What's happening? He dwelt, racking his mind for answers to far too many questions, the bus… the cameraman… the bandaged man.

This woman was showered with victims blood walking 20 feet from the bus at the time of the blast, yet a man 70 meters away was able to sustain blast damage to his clothing *without* a single drop of blood on him and had managed to acquire a head bandage all within 30 seconds of the blast?

Very peculiar, Daniel thought. *Very peculiar.*

How many other actors were on this set? He wondered as he sat silently looking around.

To his right, more medical staff had emerged from the British Medical Association headquarters and were using blankets to cover a few odd shapes on the ground.

Further down the square to his left he saw people from a building coming out to assist shocked passers-by.

'We shouldn't stick around here for too long', he explained to his silent companion as the prospect of secondary devices re-emerged and began to weigh heavy on his mind.

He helped the woman to her feet and slowly they shuffled away from the scene.

They approached a building called Lynton House whose staff were coming to peoples aid. As they reached the entrance Daniel's eyes swivelled. He realised someone was paying him attention. He glanced at the female as they passed. She was just standing there wearing a dark blouse, black skirt and shoes; but the thing most prominent about her were her eyes.

Daniel couldn't help noticing her brown eyes noticing him.

Her eyes hung on him as if imploring him, drawing him with a look that said she too required his assistance.

He suddenly felt a pang of guilt and tore his gaze away from her, returning his attention to the shocked woman at his side.

They entered the building. It was there that Daniel realised he was bleeding.

The blood came from deep cuts he'd sustained to his hands, one of which had smeared a red graffiti-like mass of blood on the back of the shocked woman's white leather coat.

One of the concierge staff guided his silent charge to a seat in the foyer and directed him to where he could go and wash the blood off. Daniel followed his directions.

As soon as the door closed behind him he found himself in another world, a world far away from the death and mayhem outside.

It was impeccably clean and dimly lit in a nice pastel shade.

A reassuring hum that came from the air-extraction unit warmed the cold silence.

Daniel stared intently at his reflection in the mirror as warm water flowed into the basin.

The grey shirt he'd laboured over that morning was covered with grisly smudges and smears making him look like he'd just finished a shift working in an abattoir.

While bathing his hands in the warm water, dissolving away blood from the cuts and lacerations on the palms of his hands he studied his reflection intently, looking for any subtle changes. Checking perhaps? Checking he was still all there.

He stared deep into his eyes, eyes that had witnessed things that could not so easily be dissolved.

'Are you sure there's nothing else I can do for you?' the overly persistent concierge asked, offering him a choice from a selection of bandages when he returned to the foyer.

'Nah, s'all right. This'll do' he replied.

His right hand had sustained the deepest wounds.

Daniel wrapped the bandage awkwardly around it and finished by using his thumb to both stem the bleeding and hold the bandage in place.

'There, I'll be okay' he said, looking around the conference facility's foyer. It now resembled an up-market accident and emergency waiting room.

He wondered what was happening outside as he wove between haphazardly laid out chairs and took one of the small bottles of water being offered to dazed looking by-passers on silver platters like complimentary flutes of champagne.

As he did, the notion of casualties put in an appearance.

His mind regressed and remerged afloat in the disfigured bus where a tally of those on the lower deck was conducted.

Soon he found himself outside on the steps making a perimeter scan of his surroundings, trying to get his bearings.

Left or right? He wondered, eyeing the flurry of activity taking place around the mangled bus.

What *do* you do in such circumstances?

Focus… try and *focus*, his weary mind urged, a mind weighed heavy with unfathomable questions.

After a blank moment his numbed brain fell back to a default. It was the same default that anyone whose mind had been conditioned in western society would automatically return to in times of death, doubt or strife.

Work.

That's it! Get back to work, he decided.

Immerse yourself in it. Bury yourself in it.

Just pick up where you left off; after all work equals normality doesn't it?

Daniel thought this, but also sensed something far beyond normality. A clear but strange version of reality had a hold on him. He relived the moment of impact on the bus again.

The bus was just over there, not far away.

Something seemed to be drawing him back.

As he ventured towards it he noticed the female he passed earlier still standing a doorway down from Lynton House.

Though numbed and shaken by events, instinct was still functional, directing him, making him an offer he gladly accepted as his feet plotted a path in her direction.

He stood facing her for a funny moment offering no words of introduction, just an exasperated shrug.

A smile of sorts was returned, as if she was somehow able to empathise with his plight.

She spoke. Saying something he didn't catch much of.

Something about a bus, she'd just missed, then all of a sudden... then something about shock, interspersed every so often with 'Are you okay?'

It was all one-way traffic bar his glum nods of agreement.

Details began to blur, losing relevance, escaping him.

His attention drifted in and out, from her brown eyes to elsewhere. From her faint freckles to a shadowy cameraman, to a place where a thousand specks of glass caught the light before falling like dying stars in a dark sky, back to the small mole just above her lip on her caramel skin.

She continued explaining how she had come to be there.

Daniel didn't care how she'd got there. He was just grateful she was there. She was calming a storm, holding back walls of destruction, shielding him from a tangle of inner forces.

She had turned the tide in a small battle that raged, in which his heart now assumed charge, dispensing with the quest for logic his mind had been grappling with.

Just the tone of her voice was enough. It was all he required.

Who needed words?

He marvelled at the very movement of her mouth, each syllable and at the whole situation.

The ominous feeling of a lurking threat abated and a sense of serenity descended upon him.

'I'm trying to get to work' he mentioned geekishly.

The words came unexpectedly, like those springing suddenly from a man who'd lain in a coma for years.

'Where do you work?' he ventured awkwardly.

'Oh, I've got to get to my agency… in Holborn' she replied.

Without taxing his brain any further or using the power of speech he presented his elbow and turned to her side-on.

She was stumped for a moment, surprised, then without a word she graciously accepted his arm with a smile and they set off walking down Tavistock Square.

'What's your name?' she asked.

'I don't even know your name!'

'Daniel' he said, as the beginnings of a smile began to protrude from one side of his face.

'Hilda!' she piped back.

As they left the square they passed the group of policemen that were assembled on the corner.

One of them kindly lifted the blue security cordon allowing them to walk beneath it arm in arm, in the direction of Holborn.

Daniel realised something unusual was happening to him as they walked. He didn't quite know what it was. All he knew was that he'd never felt like this before. It was like a strange force had enacted a change in his chemistry.

Such clarity. Everything seemed somehow more vital, more vibrant in vivid lucidity. Pink, mauve and blue geraniums in window boxes shimmered aflame. Greenery rustled gently in the light breeze exciting a lush tropical hue, even the grey Georgian building's masonry became marvellous in its intricacy, everything was evermore brilliant as they went.

He listened as Hilda enthused about how *brave* he was to have survived the bomb. A flattering idea, he thought, but one that would have to incorporate some form of mind over matter somewhere along the line.

The route to her agency took them past Russell Square in the direction of Southampton Row.

There was a high amount of police activity in evidence.

Police vans lined side streets and patrol cars streaked past every so often with sirens wailing.

They took it slow, savouring each step; moving unhurriedly on, on a different timeframe to that employed by the rest of Bloomsbury.

They moved at a pace that people were probably supposed to walk at, as society had probably done in times before the western idiom 'time *equals* money' became widely accepted. Now time equalled time.

At Southampton Row they passed a group of people huddled around a shop front watching Sky's news coverage on a large television in the window. Breaking headlines rolled across the bottom of the screen: *Reports of explosions.* The stern faced anchors seemed to say the first thing that came to mind.

An explosion near the gherkin landmark! Cut to assorted scenes of commuter chaos, cut to image of freshly halved bus.

Breaking headline: *Reports of some fatalities.*

Stern faced male anchor: We can confirm deaths have been confirmed. Bring in Sky's resident specialist 'London terror' expert *(the same ex-army idiot who justified Iraq's invasion)* to pontificate wildly.

Daniel watched the headlines trailing off the screen's edge and imagined his own captured image, beaming via satellite to a digital editing suite for modification prior to dissemination.

Hilda tugged gently at his arm, but was unable to tear him away from the image of the bus he'd been aboard 20 minutes before. With a firmer tug she managed to prise him away from the screen and they left the small crowd continuing to Holborn.

Blood trickling out from his now saturated bandage ran along the crevices in his palm.

Hilda produced a packet of tissues from her bag.

'Here...use one of these' she said, passing him the pack.

A police car sped past emitting a short yelp from its siren.

The noise eroded further the lull in anxiety he'd felt since leaving the square. Seeing the TV images of it had been an unwelcome reminder that left him feeling uneasy.

'I could do with a drink' he said gloomily, watching the small red spots expand as the tissue absorbed the blood.

'Me too' Hilda agreed.

'I need a smoke too, and to sit down... my feet!', she winced, gesturing at her sensible if slightly worn black shoes.

Thankfully, the walk of tumultuous moods neared its goal as Holborn came into view.

First they entered a chemist's to buy some new bandages.

Inside, Daniel could feel the horrified glare of a young sales assistant following him who'd noticed his blood-smeared shirt. She made a facial gesture to her colleague, when he glanced round as if signalling the order to press some imaginary panic button. Her reaction coincided with a creeping sense Daniel had felt as they'd neared Holborn. It was the sense that he'd become the focus of some unseen scrutinisers, as office workers bustled by with indifference.

The act of placing a packet of plasters, an anti-septic spray and some Fresh Mint gum on the counter made the young sales assistant's eyes bulge with fear. She froze and completely forwent asking for payment then faltered in her attempts to place the items in a bag; fumbling them nervously in the same way a lone female fumbles her car keys precisely when a machete-wielding stalker is hovering nearby.

'Thank you sir' said her supervisor, stepping in to assist his young staff member. He had made the correlation between the images replaying on the shop's wall-mounted monitors and the customer's bloodstained shirt.

Payment was handed over and change was returned accompanied by a woeful look, one expecting to glimpse traces of the terror onscreen in the customers face, but numbness had drained Daniel's face of any expression.

They left the chemist's and turned the corner in search of the nearest watering hole. The entrance to a pub called The Shakespeare's Head was situated a few doors away in the side of a large building that stood at 64-78 Kingsway.

It was still quite early, about 10:45am when they entered.

But for the barman, who stood buffing glasses in preparation for the lunchtime trade and a white whiskered old gentleman sitting in the corner, they had the place to themselves.

Hilda took a table while Daniel ordered a drink. A Jack Daniel's straight. He downed it in one then ordered two more drinks before disappearing to the restroom at the pub's rear.

There, he peeled the sodden bandage back over a basin, revealing the wound. A deep gash at the base of the little finger on his right hand was the source of most of the continued bleeding. Holding it up he stared at it in amazement, trying to equate the carnage he'd seen with the injury.

For a brief moment the antiseptic spray stung as it dissolved into the wound and congealing blood around it.

He dabbed it dry and applied the bandage as best he could. After dousing his face with cold water he popped a piece of Fresh Mint gum in his mouth and surveyed his shirt's grim appearance in the mirror.

On his return to the pub he passed the cheerful-looking old man with a white beard. He sat with a pint of ale and had a large sports holdall on the floor beside him.

Hilda sat two tables away with a glass of wine and his pint of lager in front of her. She acknowledged him with a quick smile and continued a conversation on her mobile as he sat opposite her. Over her shoulder Daniel could see onto the street outside. Sunlight shone in through the pub's open entrance casting patches of light in the doorway.

Exit, *Safety*, he thought as he made a mental note of the emergency exit sign he passed on the way back from the restroom.

As he sipped from his pint murderous scenarios massed.

The more he pondered on things the more his nerves jangled.

As Hilda's phone conversation continued he took larger and larger gulps to try and expel his jitters. His eyes began flitting between her and the entrance each time someone entered.

He tried concentrating on her, familiarising himself with the constellation of light freckles beneath her eyes and her other pleasant distractions.

She was undoubtedly pretty; pretty enough to cajole a man into seeing or doing things her way if she was so inclined. Fairly tall, of slender build her eyes had a playfulness that belied the drab blouse, skirt and frumpish shoes she wore.

Maybe he'd wrongly assumed all attractive young women working in the city spent a great deal of time and expense ensuring they wore stylish garb to work.

Not always so it seemed. He watched her take a lighter out of her bag and light a cigarette with her mobile still clasped between her ear and shoulder.

Once lit, she took a long luxurious draw, pursing her lips before blowing the smoke over his shoulder.

'Well' she said, finally snapping her phone shut.

'Well' Daniel replied, equal to the task.

'Doing anything later?' he asked wryly, leaving just enough time for her to take it literally.

'I mean... once you're done at your agency' he added.

'Er... I dunno really' she replied.

'Supposed to be going out tonight, you know... hanging with my girls.' Daniel nodded in agreement as if he knew exactly what hanging with the girls was like and looked around for inspiration of some sort or words befitting the establishment's patriarch. Hilda took another drag on her cigarette.

'On the other hand I might just stay round a friend's house'

'Yeah?' he answered.

'Depends', she added, after a moment's reflection.

'Cool', he nodded approving but not really hearing.

His attention was elsewhere, on a couple that had walked in.

The veneer of their small talk hid a mass of perplexities.

Perhaps the earlier buzz of an all time-high was a skewed reality, as here they were, in this empty place with his emptying glass. Daniel thought anxiously, even calling the volatility of the jolly seafarer's holdall, perched precariously two tables away into question.

He looked into his rapidly emptying glass. He'd come to the right place. More alcohol would help by inhibiting his powers of reasoning, powers which were becoming a destructive force, driving him towards a brain-overload in the face of the many revelations that had all been revealed in the violent space of a split second.

Hilda's shoulder bag lay on the table. It pierced the silence vibrating twice as her phone rattled against whatever it was she kept in there. She scooped out a small Nokia and studied the text message that had arrived. Daniel got up and went to the bar. The chink of coins falling into the till was heard as another pint of lager trickled out into a glass.

Of the 10 or so other customers now in the pub, he couldn't fail to notice two of them, a man and a woman.

The couple were noticeable because they did not attempt to sit down or order drinks. They both stood hovering close to the entrance, trying but failing to look inconspicuous.

Their apprehensive manner only raised his suspicions further. He glanced over at them intermittently as they did him.

The dark-haired male turned away and stood facing the window speaking in a surreptitious manner into a mobile.

His fair-haired female accomplice stood further inside the establishment glancing cautiously around every so often.

And there they both stood, him just inside the doorway, communicating and her further inside the pub keeping an eye on something or someone. Daniel took his pint back to the table, wondering what they were up to.

Were they undercover police? If they were, they didn't seem to be doing much, just watching, as if they were waiting for something to happen. No. Daniel didn't think the characters he observed were police at all. Police officers would be out looking for criminals to nab or making themselves highly visible as a deterrent, not creeping around clandestinely.

He came to the conclusion that they were probably MI5 or some other branch of British Intelligence. It wasn't too hard to imagine considering the events that had taken place earlier.

'Another white wine?' Daniel offered as he sat down.

'No I'm fine' Hilda replied, scrutinising her phones screen.

'Hang on a sec, I have to go to the ladies' she suddenly said, tossing the handset into her bag. She partially extinguished her cigarette leaving it on an ashtray then snatched her bag and left for the ladies' restroom at the pubs rear.

Daniel stared into his glass introspectively, swilling the golden fluid around as if it held the answer to his concerns regarding the inquisitive duo. His natural curiosity was allied to an anger that compelled him to confront them. Who were they and what did they want? He needed to know, if only to eliminate the new doubts in his mind springing from their appearance.

His burning gaze penetrated the back of the female's head.

She turned around sensing his deep-set eyes fixing her and flinched when he stood up abruptly.

'Whatchya lookin' at?' he muttered, taking a lumbering step forward, chuckling either at the insanity of it all or his own pending madness. Her male accomplice still with mobile pressed against ear edged towards the doorway sensing an escalation. His female counterpart's left hand clutched the bag on her shoulder more firmly but she stood her ground.

As Daniel continued forward her right hand dived inside grasping something within. She swivelled the bag from her side to her front in a manner suggesting a wrong move would have consequences.

'Pussies!' Daniel hissed. She stood motionless; her steely eyes were transfixed, frozen with fear of what she might do next. Daniel just stood there then chuckled. It was utter madness. After already dicing with death once that morning his curiosity didn't extend to finding out if she was scared enough of a slightly inebriated bus bomb survivor to consider levelling her firearm at him, let alone pulling the trigger.

For a furious moment he *glowered* at her then raising the glass he was holding to his lips he drank the remaining lager and slammed the empty glass down on the table in front of her.

Casting her a look of utter contempt, he turned away and saw Hilda had returned from the restroom.

She was standing with her back to him near the bearded seafarer making another call on her mobile.

Hilda ended the call and spun round as he approached.

The corners of her mouth curled up into a smile, a smile made all the more succulent by newly applied lip-gloss.

'Get yer stuff!' Daniel ordered, hastily signalling his readiness to move. Hilda stubbed out her cigarette and picked up her bag without saying a word.

They left the pub and crossed the road between a burst of fast flowing traffic once it had given way to near silence.

The silence was quiet enough for the pips of the pelican crossing to be heard as empty bus lanes devoid of everything but the odd black cab brought an unfamiliar hush to High Holborn.

The short distance they walked from the pub to her agency in Southampton Place was a nervous affair.

Daniel could sense something was not right.

Since the incident in the pub his vigilance had given way to a rising sense of paranoia that sought answers to a growing number of nagging questions.

Somehow Hilda contained her annoyance as he gave a litterbin surrounded by bags of dumped refuse a wide berth, veering sideways and dragging her along with him.

His eyes flitted from pedestrian to pedestrian, eking out and fixing any whose look strayed fractionally beyond the cursory with a scrutinising glare.

Thankfully, a short time later Hilda pressed the buzzer on the door of an unassuming Georgian terrace at 13 Southampton Row as Daniel tentatively surveyed the street around.

They were at the offices of her agency, *Witan Jardine.*

The building's frontage belied the sleek contemporary interior they met across the threshold when the door release buzzed, allowing them to enter.

Inside, the receptionist acknowledged their presence after a longish wait.

'Yes?' she said, rather tersely, looking up from her computer.

'Oh, hi I'm here to see Cheun' she said.

'And you are?' enquired the receptionist.

'Hilda… Hilda Edionseri' she replied.

The receptionist punched something into her keyboard then a colleague arrived ushering them up some stairs and along a hallway past a number of cubicles.

They were shown into one where they sat down. After some time a sharp suited man of oriental appearance arrived.

'Hilda… are you okay?' he inquired in a concerned tone, as he shut the door behind him.

'Cheun…yeah I'm fine, I just missed the bus, I was *so* lucky.'

This is Daniel', she said, motioning towards the figure the eastern gentleman had eyed with concealed circumspect.

'My knight in shining armour' she gushed.

'He was *actually on* the bus!' she enthused excitedly, clasping her arm around his and wiggling in her seat as if he were a prize catch.

'Oh, hi there, are you alright?' said the easterner whose hovering hand decided a handshake was perhaps unnecessary.

'Is there anything I can get you?' he asked.

'No, I'm fine' Daniel replied, but eventually he accepted a can of Coke just to end the cycle of insistence that was a further drag on a part of his brain presently concerned with less mundane matters.

'I'm told no public transport is running in central London at the moment, so what do you guys intend doing?' Cheun asked, after returning with the beverage.

'We can wait here for a bit? Hilda suggested hopefully.

'Fine…no problem, wait here for the time being' he replied.

'And if there's anything you need, just ask' he said and he left them in each other's company.

What a strange day it had been. A strange day so far, he thought, trying to recline in the chair, but its efficient modern styling wouldn't permit any more than an acute degree of comfort. It was 12:38pm according to Hilda's watch.

And here he sat, held captive by a breakdown in London's transport infrastructure, captivated by a stranger, sharing words and experiences.

Time flew by, time in which they laughed, hugged, reminisced like old school friends and exchanged mobile numbers.

They spoke about secondary school in South London, both being Nigerian, the job she'd had for the last 4 years, his goals for the next four, ex-boyfriends who wanted her back and ex-girlfriends he never wanted to set eyes on again.

The conversation continued till the receptionist appeared bearing a gift. She presented Daniel with a promotional white T-shirt bearing the agencies *Witan Jardine* logo.

'Great, just what I've always wanted' He replied, trying to inject some humour into the sterile white-walled cubicle.

He went to change, bundling his bloodstained shirt into his gym-sack and returned from the restroom 5 minutes later to find Hilda's bag still on the table but no sign of her.

He sat down and waited for her. The minutes ticked by.

As they passed he began to await her return with concern.

Any time away from her seemed to allow an anxious energy to creep up on him.

He tried reassuring himself as he stared out of the window monitoring the rooftops of High Holborn and the scene below in both directions.

Traffic seemed to be springing back to some level of normality when Hilda re-appeared thirty minutes later.

'Where'd you go?' he asked, as soon as she sat down, trying his best not to sound too much like a suspicious husband.

'I uh, had to make a phone call, babes'

'Oh… right' Daniel said, ruminating.

41

Hilda rummaged around in her bag taking out her mobile and glancing at its screen.

'So you're heading south… to Brixton?' He said, changing the direction of the conversation.

'I can come with you… to keep you safe' he chuckled.

'But I thought you live in North London, babes?'

'I do, but I've gotta go south today anyway'

'I'm meeting up with a few mates later on' he said, saying whatever it took to ensure the time with her continued.

He said this because Hilda's very presence was sanctuary.

Far from being a damsel in distress, she was an angel, *his* angel, saving him by just being there, listening to him, lightly dismissing his fears like an adult does a child's feverish imagination. She had been there for him when a strange cocktail of emotions tossed him between feeling spiritually invincible, mentally vulnerable and physically weak.

Later, by 2:45pm practically all traffic except public transport was back to normal in central London.

Hilda closed the door behind them as they set out on a daunting walk, joining the exodus of stranded city-workers making an early start on the long walk home.

They made their way down Farringdon Road, arms intertwined in a leisurely promenade and stopped at a Chinese restaurant on the way where they had a bite to eat.

Then they set off again, crossing Blackfriars Bridge from North to South London.

Halfway across they rested for a while allowing Hilda to give her aching feet a rest while Daniel stood gazing downriver towards Docklands. Its steel structures gleamed large on the horizon, glinting in the afternoon sun.

~Chapter 4~

Be Vigilant, Be Very Vigilant

His morning routine would be different today. Daniel became aware of this the moment he stirred and realised where he was. He woke up in his brother's old bedroom in a semi-detached house in south London.

It was Friday the 8th of July, the day after.

The demons of the previous day had been warded off by a combination of mental exhaustion and the contents of three empty lager cans that lay strewn around the bedside.

Today's look would be a makeshift one, he thought, holding up a white shirt with a thin blue line checking through it.

It was a more humble affair, a slightly crumpled caste-off that had been languishing in a wardrobe.

The first dilemma, he thought as he scratched his head was that it required cufflinks.

The scuffing his shoes had sustained was quite noticeable and he hoped the a numerous small holes on his trousers knees where he'd dragged himself through glass strewn across the shattered bus's floor were not as prominent.

Rolling up the sleeves solved the problem of the shirt, but as he passed a mirror and had to concede he would get some funny looks today.

Daniel set off down a tree-lined road to catch a bus taking large gulps of air in all its significance.

With a new day upon him, he offered up thanks and a smile welcoming it. All seemed as it should be as he turned the corner at the end of the road.

He spent a nervy bus ride to Brixton leaning against the bus driver's cab. Passengers shoved past him to grab seats as the bus filled. He felt the remaining can of lager in his bag as he scanned their faces. Each one was wrapped up in their daily fight to reach their occupations.

Life went on Daniel supposed, but he couldn't help thinking their blank expression were similar to the blood-spattered woman's blast-induced state of shock, after victims' remnants had rained down around her.

'We'd like to remind all passengers to be vigilant in this period of heightened security', came the announcement.

Those aboard the tube train ready to depart Brixton waited.

A sizeable African woman closed her eyes and clutched a small bible to her chest as the doors shut. Throughout the carriage nervous facial expressions indicative of a raised state of anxiety mirrored the headlines that leapt from the pages of their newspapers. They were terrified, *literally*.

Each time the train stopped and its doors opened they peered up in unison, scanning faces, luggage and facial hair length before breathing a collective sigh of relief.

Phew! It was safe, safe to continue reading of the lurking terror threatening the very transport network they sat upon. Some of the theories the press put forward left a whiff of doubt, but the reports succeeded in heightening the air of anxiety, ensuring *terror* hit home with the accuracy of a targeted marketing campaign, striking fear into hearts and minds.

Calls for *vigilance* were positioned alongside terrifying tales, recounted by those caught up in the previous days mayhem.

Vigilance could have been the name of the latest fragrance. Launched July 7th: *Vigilance* ~ A chic form of paranoia.

But a few squirts of it would not disguise the rampant fear permeating London's transport network, infecting those whose livelihoods depended on it.

As the tube reached Vauxhall station the can of lager was opened in a clandestine manner.

The muted 'Piffftt' it made raised some eyebrows and brought him a few looks of indignation. Daniel took furtive gulps knowing that while he couldn't prevent these instantaneous judgments, the British belief also prohibited most forms of intervention; not that he was too bothered either way.

His slightly dishevelled appearance allied with the fact that he was drinking a can of Stella Artois at 8.35am in the morning onboard a train to work was precisely the kind of situation strangers, particularly commuters avoided at all costs.

Daniel reflected on his new temporary categorisation.

It was probably not too dissimilar to that of the crazy person who begins a tirade the moment the tube doors slid shut. Everyone had come across one at least once.

Their remonstrating grew louder and more vociferous the more their captive audience avoided eye contact and acted as if they weren't there. Were such people stark raving mad?

Or did they just need someone, anyone, to listen to them?

Watching the faces staring resolutely ahead Daniel began to get an idea about just how they might feel.

But this morning's madness didn't matter. It was nothing in comparison to the complete insanity of the previous day.

What mattered was the future. His future, and that he lived to *think* another day.

The warm fluid dulled the edge of his jagged thoughts in a fuzzy haze and he began to feel less anxious.

The need to mentally probe and verify each passenger within a 20-foot radius subsided.

The empty can was discarded on the floor in a petulant show of defiance for those of the disapproving gazes.

Daniel returned a smile to a seated blonde woman who saw the funny side of it or had been living in a news black hole for the past 24 hours.

Asians, anyone remotely swarthy looking and people dressed in non-western attire were fixed with accusing stares.

The stares turned into resolutely unapologetic looks in the direction of fellow travellers, in the hope they too shared similar concerns. Most shrank into looks of embarrassment on realising they'd deemed an Asian woman of advancing years waistline to constitute a bomb threat.

The passengers rode their luck until the train reached Pimlico.

As the doors slid open the uneasy nervousness gave way to what can only be described as all-out panic.

A Somali gentleman staggered aboard, struggling with the largest suitcase imaginable.

Eyes widened and gasps were heard, but no one dared say anything in a fine display of British mettle. Those standing by the doors hurriedly voted with their feet, preferring to try their luck with the next train.

In that instant Daniel noticed a tiny change in Western values. The expression *'better late than never'* now held sway over *'Time equals money'*.

He cast an eye over a passenger's copy of The Daily Express.

'WE BRITONS SHALL NEVER BE DEFEATED' read the headline in all its Churchillian bluster.

Its masthead, consisting of a crusader brandishing a sword and shield bearing the cross of Saint George had added poignancy.

Daniel whipped the paper off the seat when the man reading it disembarked at Victoria and turned to the pages with coverage of the Tavistock Square bomb. He was cursorily tracing down the page where survivors were recounting close brushes with death when his pulse suddenly began to race.

'Wait, no... never!' he mouthed silently, stunned by what he was reading. His beating heart amplified, reaching an audible thud that pounded against his temple.

Stay calm he told himself.

There *must* be a logical explanation... there always is.

Hunched over the newspaper he looked cautiously around at the passengers nearby before reading the paragraph again.

The article said that two female survivors who were onboard the bus that exploded in Tavistock Square identified a man on the lower deck as the bomber.

They relayed this to a nurse called Terence Musata who treated them for shock at University College Hospital.

What this meant wasn't immediately clear to Daniel, but more room for doubt and conjecture was opening up.

Confusion it seemed was set to reign.

He poured over the page searching for any description, vague or otherwise of this *bomber*, knowing that the bus driver and himself were the only men on the lower deck at the time of the explosion.

Why did the women think he had been the bomber?

He remembered the abject fear in their eyes as they huddled together on the floor.

Surely it wasn't *him* they feared moments after the blast?

Sighing wearily he read on. The rest of the article focused on quotes from a 61-year-old man called Richard Jones.

Jones claimed he was onboard the bus shortly before it exploded but got off after becoming agitated by the behaviour of a man he described as having a dark-skinned complexion, who kept dipping into a bag.

The swish of the tube's doors opening brought Daniel to his senses. Stuffing the newspaper in his bag he jumped up.

He had to put the disconcerting article to the back of his mind. Along the platform to the escalator he went, determined to face the day ahead, just as the slogan from the newspaper had bellowed.

'Un-cowed And Standing Proud!'

Daniel strode out of the lift on the 6th floor of Transworld House, one of the tall office blocks surrounding Old Street's busy roundabout. He passed through the swinging doors imagining the jovial atmosphere of the pub during lunch.

That would probably be the best time to make yesterday's events the topic of conversation.

At his desk he switched on his screen and sipped the grande mocha he'd bought from the Prêt A Manger across the road.

In the quiet moments before the office began to fill he thought about the newspaper article.

Soon his cursor was hovering over the links on a news website.

Within a click he was scouring through a raft of stories recounting the havoc and horror wrought by the bombings.

Articles concerning the bus bombing came in for particular scrutiny, as did survivors' accounts of the moments that followed.

He clicked through an image gallery showing the mangled bus from different aspects. It was an iconic image that had already begun to symbolise a point in British history christened 7/7.

Microsoft Outlook sat open on his screen giving some semblance of industry as office staff began arriving en-masse.

To those interested he appeared to be organising data reports and feedback for the following Monday's meeting, but his mind was elsewhere, far away, caught in an altered state where the meeting seemed immaterial, belonging to a disordered world that only served to shroud the reality.

The share price information normally rolling along the screen above the marketing department desks was also given over to the fevered quest for news.

Today it screened images of Kings Cross the previous day where the walking wounded, a patched-up, bloodied army of commuters, trooped past cameras like war-weary Crimean foot-soldiers returning from the front, in Reality TV's latest cruel twist - Reality Warfare: War To Your Door.

Daniel had been anticipating a response to the text message he sent Hilda. It was the one positive thing he felt he had going for him today, balancing out the drabness of the office on a Monday and his concerns about the article he'd read.

His text suggested they meet up for lunch the following week. She said her office was in Moorgate, about 15 minutes away from his in Old Street.

Ten minutes later she hadn't responded.

Fair enough, he thought. This time lapse was within the most intimate level of text message response times.

Nearly an hour later Daniel drummed his fingers on the desk.

Hilda still hadn't replied.

Maybe she was busy? He assumed, hopefully.

It was either that or the text fell into a 3rd category; her phone was off and she would reply to his text later that evening.

He certainly hoped this was the case, as the final category didn't bear thinking about.

The idea that his text message went the way of annoying network messages; dealt with, with a swift press of the delete button crossed his mind.

His productivity for the rest of that morning remained fairly low and the slightly raised inter-cranial pressure he'd felt arriving at work that morning increased another notch as the minutes before noon ticked slowly by.

An hour later he returned to the office with a Marks & Spencer's salmon pasta salad and an overpriced fruit juice.

He spent the rest of his lunch snatching mouthfuls between pouring over links Google returned for the words 'Tavistock Square' and 'bus'. Every link he clicked he found an image of the bombed bus that had been irrevocably burned into his mind. The instantly recognisable wrecked bus was being branded into public consciousness.

Personal accounts of the previous days events were numerous. Daniel looked for anything that might confirm what he'd seen and heard that day. He read on totally transfixed. The words onscreen seemed to ignite in turn, exploding in meaning and significance as the realisation slowly grew that what he'd witnessed could be important to the investigation.

He could help piece together a more complete picture of what happened! Soon many browser windows were open and he began scribbling down notes, crosschecking details with reports on other sites.

1. Tania Calabrese was aboard the bus with boyfriend Tony Cancellera, when she noticed policemen blocking off the street seconds before the explosion.

2. A traffic warden standing across the road called Adesoji Adesi reported that the bus driver was asking him for directions when the explosion occurred.

3. A bike courier called Andrew Childes saw a black man running away from the bus seconds after it exploded.

Daniel noticed a discrepancy in an account attributed to the same person on different websites.

He pressed the F5 button to refresh the browser and saw the article change before his eyes.

Surprised, he pressed F5 again and he saw it happen again.

The accounts were being changed as he was reading them!

Quickly he began cutting and pasting text from each account of the bus bomb's aftermath from each browser into a text editor to print off before they disappeared for good.

The media coverage was already altering, beginning to form one amalgam out of the deluge of differing accounts that had sprung forth the previous day.

Later that afternoon he picked the vibrating Nokia up off his desk. Examining its face he scoured his memory until the last three digits brought to mind a more recognisable one, the face of a relative. She was calling to tell him the death toll from the bus was 14 and not 2 as the previous days TV reports stated.

'Uh' Daniel replied, not really knowing what he was supposed to do with this morbid statistic.

Statistics usually meant nothing beyond marketing tools, but this was the first one that ever hit him with such immediacy.

He did the math. It represented a 700% increase in carnage, a death rate-rise at a terrible rate.

It meant things were still changing, in a state of flux.

Could they get any worse? He asked himself, somehow feeling the evil force he'd escaped hadn't dissipated but was still out there lurking, waiting to engulf him.

'Hello…?', repeated his relative at the other end of the line.

'Are you okay? Are you *sure* you're okay?'

'Maybe you should book an appointment with your G.P… just in case' she advised.

'You've contacted the police, haven't you?' Daniel didn't answer. Part of him knew certain forces would be in touch with him at some stage. According to details Deputy Assistant Commissioner Peter Clarke had given at a press briefing that morning their investigations were well underway.

If Clarke was to be believed then any one of 2000 detectives and 550 officers drafted in to support what he called the *'largest criminal investigation in U.K history'* would contact him soon.

The phone remained pressed against Daniel's ear some time after the faint pop indicated the conversations end.

The parameters of his deducing had altered once again.

The memory of a familiar darkened setting of a bus beckoned. The three women lay aghast with accusing glares. He relived the moment again, this time in the knowledge that many more souls had begun a different journey in that terrible instant.

Daniel looked up from his screen as open laughter echoed from the hallway. It was the IT guys returning from lunch at The Litten Tree pub sharing a final gag as they entered the office.

The hilarity settled to a more amenable level by the time they reached their desks, to a level more conducive to an office on a Friday afternoon in the senior manager's absence.

With a sigh Daniel hit the return key, firing and forgetting email responses. He was leaving a digital trail, evidence he'd lifted a finger that day. The energy this small act expended seemed life sapping and soon he was gathering up the folders on his desk and placing them in his bag.

He had come to work to put it all to the back of his mind but found concentration increasingly difficult. Now he couldn't sit here and not be affected by the tangle of emotions now he'd been told the full death toll of the horror he escaped.

Daniel's progress towards the lift was not as brisk as it had been on the way in that morning. It was as though an unseen burden placed upon him had grown. His chest heaved while the lift descended. Slow and deep inhalations fought to ward off an inner response that threatened to break cover.

The back of his sleeve wiped away the wetness from his eyes as he exited the building and disappeared down steps into the underground. He tried to straighten himself out by taking deep breaths. Ahead he saw the blue strap on the shoulder of a young blonde female indicating her rank of C.S.O.

The Community Support Officer stood in the underground station, part of the highly visible police presence reassuring and protecting the public from marauding suicide bombers.

Presently she was coyly rebuffing the advances of a market trader taking a break from tending one of the nearby stalls.

Daniel approached them, swallowing a lump in his throat.

'Excuse me... I need to... provide a statement' he said.

After an awkward moment as a third party to their small talk they both turned to acknowledge him with vacant smiles.

'To report an incident. I need to provide a police statement', he blurted, thinking they were aware of what had taken place the previous day.

'Ahh, the old bill. In a spot of bovver, mate?' quipped the market trader beaming.

'Well you want the right exit, head towards Finsbury Square. It's on the left!', he declared triumphantly, before the young blonde could respond.

Though flattered by his overtures, any suggestion that she needed his help in performing her duties spurred her to offer the sullen inquisitor directions of her own. She put the market trader back in his place, fixing him with a satisfied smile as Daniel turned, following her directions.

He passed the early evening traffic threading its way down City Road on his way to Shoreditch Police station.

That was where he would provide a statement, a statement that would completely absolve him from the faintly ridiculous notion that he was *the bus bomber.*

He would get it over and done with, right now, providing *vital* witness information in what was labelled the largest criminal investigation in U.K history and this nightmare would be over, today.

As he saw the police station up ahead his walk slowed to a more ponderous pace.

Different scenarios and the possible ramifications that may result from the step he was about to take loomed up on him.

For the first time he asked himself, had he actually thought through what was he going to tell them?

Yes officer, I saw two unmarked vehicles holding up the bus.

The driver of the first car directed a police motorcyclist to leave the scene before diverting the bus to Tavistock Square minutes later.

Something about his account didn't rest too easily with him.

Something about the way his image had been captured in Tavistock Square concerned him, as did the other strange things he saw prior to and following the blast.

After hesitating outside the police station for a bit, he entered. Maybe it's best to get it over and done with, he thought.

Inside the station he prodded a button on the front desk.

Its buzz signalled an end to his procrastination and after a short period of time a female officer appeared.

'Hi, I've come… I need to make a statement' he re-phrased.

'Concerning?' her raised tone added the necessary faux concern.

'Concerning a crime' he replied, matter of factly.

The officer responded by taking out a large logbook and laid it out on the desk in front of her with a faint sigh.

'And when did this take place, this crime?'

'Er, yesterday… July the 7th' he offered tentatively, interested to see her expression once she grasped the gravity of the matter his enquiry concerned.

'And were there any injuries… or casualties?' she asked, awaiting his response pen poised above pad.

'Yes' he replied, nodding morosely.

'Location…?'

'On a bus… in Tavistock Square. On a number 30 bus.'

The officer took a discerning glance at him then seemed to consult her memory for a moment.

'Right then' she announced, snapping the book shut.

'Won't be a moment' she sang as she marched off.

After some deliberation she returned a while later and handed him a slip with a telephone number scrawled on it.

'There you go' she said, sounding relieved.

'That's the Anti-Terrorist hotline number… give them a call'

Daniel stared at the note as she scuttled off to tend to other more pressing matters. He was slightly confused but in an odd way he felt kind of relieved as he walked back to Old Street.

The 4th Bomb

An Asian keeper of a newsagent's he entered on the way began to regard him with annoyance, but more concerned with other things, Daniel ignored him and continued skimming through the newspapers on display.

Eventually he went up to the counter and paid the shopkeeper. 'Sun, Mirror, Star, Telegraph, Guardian and Evening Standard' said the shopkeeper totalling them up, now less dismissive as he hazarded a guess as to what his customer's preoccupation with the news might be.

By the time Daniel arrived back at his apartment it was 6.30pm. He entered the 4-digit code to gain access to the basement and took the elevator up to his abode. He entered, dropping his bag on the floor as the door shut behind him.

Although bathed in rays from a descending sun, it's white walls and spartan décor now had a coldness about them.

Something had changed. Around him things appeared much as he'd left them on Thursday morning.

He paused.

Thursday. It seemed a lifetime away. So much had happened; so much had changed irrevocably since then.

He went from room to room, casting an eye around the place, reacquainting himself with its space. Kicking off his battle-worn shoes he laid spread-out on the bed and rested.

He opened his eyes, staring up at the white ceiling and wondered. Perhaps nothing had changed in the time he'd been away from it, nothing except him.

After going through the pile of newspapers he'd bought, a duvet he'd dragged from the bedroom into the lounge covered him. His belt slipped from his waist onto the floor beside him and he lay coiled in a semi-foetal position on the couch.

Despite a state of mental fatigue his eyes remained glued to the television fizzing away in front of him.

It's rolling updates re-confirmed reports that had been confirmed minutes before. The process was repeated in 15 minutes cycles, on the hour every hour, mixing witness accounts with reports from 'sources', melding speculation with theory and compounding them all into one thick consistency for the public's consumption.

Daniel found the changing reports all the more compelling. This curse, the experience that hung over him like a dark cloud acted as a filter to the speculation and confusion he watched creeping into the picture the media was painting.

He continued watching but a strong element of doubt remained, doubts raised by the cracks in reality he saw on the pavement of Tavistock Square.

He wanted to know. He needed to know.

He felt a mad rush to understand before slumber interceded, so he could awaken refreshed without the flashbacks and questions that plagued his waking thoughts.

But this was one night when he would not put the world to rights through heated debate or structured thinking.

As darkness fell his eyelids grew heavy. A yawn greeted the umpteenth running of footage showing an evacuee clutching her face. She looked like *The Phantom Of The Opera*.

The heavier his eyelids became, the more dream-like the reality of the past 48 hours seemed. Drifting somewhere between consciousness and slumber, he seemed to meld with the sprites flickering inside the liquid crystal display. They beckoned him closer, enticing him with a glimpse of secrets held within, promising to reveal truths that governed the true reality.

Saturday Morning, July 9th

A faint drone stirred him. Daniel tucked his head under the duvet, shielding his eyes from the sunlight that streamed in heralding the arrival of another day.

The noise gradually became more recognisable as the sound of the television.

Politicians were debating the threat posed to public safety by Tony Blair's belief in the *War On Terror*.

Half groaning, half yawning, Daniel sat up rubbing his eyes. He, of all people didn't need the political point scoring disturbing his internal dialogue first thing in the morning.

The muscles in his upper back flexed as his clenched fists stretched skyward embracing the new day.

His parched throat gave rise to a quick mental scan of fluids in the fridge, conjuring up the image of a milk carton.

Vaulting up off the sofa he opened the fridge door and held the carton aloft till the last drop trickled onto his tongue.

In the bedroom he rummaged through clothes piled on the floor of the wardrobes, pulling out a crumpled pair of light grey tracksuit bottoms.

A strategic sniff told him they were not particularly fragrant but as they didn't reek, he pulled them on with a white T-shirt. After putting on his trainers he made his way out of the apartment. He opened the front door; just then he glimpsed a figure walking past. He stepped outside and saw a man disappearing down the hallway as he shut the door.

Hmm, probably someone visiting a resident, he thought, wondering if it was one of the undesirables his retired neighbour Vera was always crowing on about.

Outside his apartment block he skipped down the steps, turned left and strolled the short distance to the corner.

At the end of the road the green expanse of Enfield Town Park could be seen through its park gates extending down to the stream and up to Bush Hill golf course.

It was early so it was still quiet enough for him to be accompanied by the dawn chorus's stragglers.

Daniel walked up to its black wrought iron gates. There he stretched and limbered-up in preparation for a morning jog.

The sound of ducks quacking carried on the wind that blustered about his ears as a canter turned into a brisk jog.

By the time he reached the tennis courts and began up a slight incline he was steadily sucking in gulps of air on a route leading to a gravel path that ran beside the stream.

Daniel swept past a man walking his dog and negated his usual route across the footbridge and up around the perimeter of the golf course to suffice with a single lap of the park.

He ducked under low hanging branches in his path on the far side then paced himself over the long flat stretch to the war memorial and turned for the final leg home.

Gasping for breath he stooped down, clutching the iron railings of the park gate. His legs were spent.

Beads of sweat trickled down the back of his neck as he glanced at his watch. Not bad, he gauged.

Looking up he noticed the figure he'd passed on the final leg of his run still leaning innocuously against a park fence.

The man didn't appear to be engaged in any sort of early morning pursuit, such as jogging or dog walking, he'd just been standing there watching and waiting.

The figure suddenly put on a pair of dark shades then began walking towards the gates. Daniel's panting quickly subsided. He followed the stranger's progress intently.

Something about it didn't feel right. Although curious Daniel didn't think it wise to hang about waiting to find out what, as the man advanced up the incline towards him.

As soon as the man was halfway to the park gates Daniel suddenly took off.

Like a shot he went, going 20, 30 meters and more heading down towards the tennis courts.

He glanced across at the figure who spun 180 degrees and was now heading briskly *back* to his initial position.

Scanning the horizon ahead for signs of anything untoward, Daniel zoned in on a figure standing on the footbridge.

It could be anyone, he rationalised, a dog walker... someone feeding the ducks, perhaps?

Daniel slowed down, turned and began walking back towards the park gates, this time maintaining a steady gaze on the man across the green who again, changed his direction and began walking towards the park gates.

This time Daniel studied the figure carefully.

European male, around 6 foot tall, 30'ish, wearing three-quarter length shorts and a Fred Perry style short-sleeve top.

Daniel reached the park gates first and exited through the vehicle entrance. His ears became alert to the sound of footsteps crunching up the gravel behind him.

As he glanced over his shoulder, the urgent squeal of brakes sounded.

Instinctively he swerved out of the way of an MPV that jolted to a halt directly in front of him, narrowly avoiding the vehicle's bonnet.

He continued briskly past, briefly glimpsing two occupants through partially lowered darkened windows.

Something told him to walk on without challenging the driver. He was aware that something stranger than mere reckless driving was afoot, something that was somehow related to the events of two days before.

By the time he reached the corner his walk quickened and he jogged the remaining distance to his block's entrance.

The sound of the MPV's engine revving wildly as it reversed up the cul-de-sac behind him made him look over his shoulder. Hurriedly, he punched in his entry code and took the staircase back up to his apartment.

Inside he slammed the door, kicked off his trainers and turned on the shower in the en-suite bathroom.

His brain performed a raft of background processes.

The notion seemed faintly ridiculous.

The powerful spray tingled his face.

It had never seriously crossed his mind.

Apart from one second's hesitation before he leapt from the bombed bus, he'd never seriously thought he might actually be considered a suspect.

Surely, if he were *really* a suspect he'd be face down, hands trussed behind his back with an automatic firearm pointed at his head... or worse. Yet this piece of logic did not explain the behaviour of the trio he'd just encountered.

Confusion swirled around his head.

Something didn't add up. Something that didn't square with the trio's menacing behaviour.

A hot spray rinsed the soapy lather from his face.

He scrubbed his body, ruminating over the new element of uncertainty that had entered the equation.

The driver of the MPV. He was wearing a dark blue jacket.

It had appeared innocuous enough at the time... the man bolting off down the corridor as he'd left earlier that morning had also been wearing a dark blue jacket!

What had they been up to? What was their aim?

One thing was becoming very apparent to him.

Something strange and troubling was bubbling away and where and when it would rear its head again he wasn't sure.

~Chapter 5~

A New Norm

Later a distinct feeling had welled up within him. It probably began the moment he sensed his morning jog might've proved less than beneficial to him health-wise.

The feeling had grown during the course of Saturday into a slow anger he recognised burning somewhere deep and distant.

Initially his response to 7/7 acquiesced with the same tidal wave of emotion all Londoner's felt, even after his close brush with death.

He was among the survivors, many of whom joyfully proclaimed themselves *lucky to be alive*, but joy was an emotion Daniel was unable to share. Amid the love and concern shown, by friends and family he felt aloof and alone.

The more he sat watching news of the attacks and politicians sombre posturing the more the feeling grew.

The bombings received blanket coverage on all the news channels yet hardly any factual details seemed to be forthcoming. Instead more theories seemed to spring from media sources, adding to the misgivings he had about the sequence of events he witnessed that morning.

By following the news ardently he'd hoped to eliminate these doubts, but found the opposite to be the case.

The doubts he had were growing.

He flicked between channels wondering why the police had confirmed only two fatalities on the Tavistock Square bus on July 7th when they were able to confirm six at Edgware and seven at Aldgate underground stations the same day.

It seemed odd. But everything he was watching felt surreal.

It was comparable to when he'd sat for hours transfixed by the image of the falling twin towers on 9/11, except now the events iconic image related to him, *personally*.

He had to keep reminding himself it was not a figment of his imagination. The bus had been *real* and he'd been on it.

He had to hold on to something real, just to keep a level head and a grip on reality. What he really needed was *someone* real.

Right now isolation was becoming his most pressing problem, being isolated with the unsettling questions occupying his mind and plaguing his thoughts.

Hilda came to mind.

She would understand, he thought, idly scrolling through the names in his Nokia's contact list.

She was the only person that could see his point of view, but she wasn't within reach. Yet.

The dust had settled. It was the calm before the media storm. On television footage of the stoic scenes outside Kings cross were repeated. Shrill reports echoed, the Union flag fluttered at half-mast. In the capital's hour of peril they depicted a picture of unity.

'United We Stand' was the line. Cameras panned across the faces of Londoner's carefully including the faces of Africans, Sikhs and Muslim bus drivers among the sea of solemn white faces. The recriminations had yet to begin and the ramifications the attacks would have on the future way of life and possible manner of death of Londoner's had yet to hit home.

Daniel stared blankly at the ceremony still pondering his earlier brush with the three men that morning.

He flicked channels restlessly. On one channel the idea of a 5th bomber still at large with more lethal luggage was floated.

He would cross that bridge when he got there, he imagined, taking the news item and his earlier encounter to an ultimate conclusion.

Later that evening he scanned his surroundings furtively.

It was a Saturday night in the West End.

He stood on the Charing Cross Road outside the Windham Theatre, adjacent to Stringfellows nightclub where he arranged to meet Brian.

They would have a meal with some of Brian's work colleagues in a Soho restaurant they would go onto a nightclub.

Daniel chose the meeting place knowing it was a vantage point that had all of Leicester Square's underground exits covered.

When the appointed time of 8.15pm came and went there was no sign of a normally punctual Brian. As time passed with no sign of his friend his nerves began to fray.

The congested traffic stopped and started. Slick sports cars swerved past and some rude boys banging Hip-Hop beats at a high volume rolled through in coupes.

Daniel regarded his watch with a look of disdain.

'Where the hell?' he huffed.

The possibility that the call he made to Brian arranging to meet could have been monitored played on his mind. He felt edgy. Was he in danger? He wondered. In danger of what?

He wasn't too sure but waiting here was adding to the doubts.

They were the reason he'd called Brian to arrange a night out, to get *away from the doubts,* because Brian always knew what was going on on the social scene.

Daniel scanned in all directions. He realised he would've felt a lot safer meeting-up inside the restaurant.

He had to assume he was probably being watched.

He certainly got the feeling he was. But watched by whom?

If Friday's newspapers were to be believed and this *was* the largest ever investigation in UK history, his every move could already be being tracked.

Daniel peered cautiously upwards at the windows above street level then surveyed the street for CCTV cameras.

His gaze was met by a sea of faces. In them he looked for traces, any sign, any hint that would give away those observing instead of swerving through the crowds that ebbed and flowed in all directions. But unlike his, they were unburdened by the fear of homemade or weapons-grade explosives or men in pursuit causing feverish speculations.

'Just stay calm' he urged himself, tapping his foot impatiently.

The 4th Bomb

After an anxious half hour wait, a familiar face emerged from the exit of Leicester Square underground station.

Though peeved by his lateness Daniel was pleased to see him. Brian spotted Daniel across the road and nodded a smile as he waited for the traffic to halt.

After the meal, the group left the restaurant and jostled among revellers on their way to a club in nearby Covent Garden.

It was then that Daniel chose to tell Brian what he'd wanted to say over the phone earlier that day but hadn't.

'I was aboard the bus' he began.

'Huh... what bus?' answered Brian wondering what on earth his friend was talking about.

'The number 30 bus' Daniel replied.

'In Tavistock Square'

'Oh' nodded Brian, still nonplussed.

'The one that got blown up' Daniel reiterated.

'Oh... were you? *Really*?' asked Brian peering cautiously round at his friend.

'Where did you get off?' he quizzed after a pregnant pause.

'I didn't... I was on it' came the reply.

'Before it exploded?' asked Brian, confused.

'Before *and* after the bomb exploded' Daniel stressed.

'I ran after the bomb went off' he said, recognising the doubtful look appearing on Brian's face. It was a look Daniel knew he would soon become familiar with.

Brian looked away, taking a moment to garner logic before returning to his friend.

'Did you see the bomber?' he asked. Daniel sighed.

'I was downstairs. The bomb exploded upstairs.'

He could almost hear the cogs in Brian's brain whirring as something dawned.

'You believe me, don't you?' He asked.

No reply came.

Daniel realised it was probably wrong for him to expect Brian to instantly believe him minutes after learning he was on the ill-fated bus. Though Brian was his friend it was too much to expect, too quick. It was a small lesson.

He would have to adopt a more gradual approach.

It takes real evidence gleaned over a period time for people to understand, let alone believe. Anyway, tonight he was meant to put it all to the back of his mind and that was what he decided to do, as they arrived in Covent Garden.

~Chapter 6~

A Tale Of Two Londoners

Nursing a dull throbbing headache, Daniel dozed the excesses of the night before off on the couch in the lounge.

It had become his surrogate bed of late, providing him with a constant supply of rolling news updates while the duvet and the warm hum of the TV kept him company.

Not too far away in another part of North London was Rachel. She sat in the quiet surrounds of her garden on what was a pleasant Sunday afternoon.

The meandering drone of bees lazily probing bushes of lavender could be heard above the faint rustle of leaves.

Copious amounts of tea hadn't fully erased the taste of smoke from her throat and nose just as whisky the night before hadn't silenced the echoed screams of terrified passengers.

She poured herself another whisky shortly after the Anti-Terrorist detectives departed. They had arrived at her home that morning to take a witness statement from her as part of the investigation into what took place aboard the bombed Piccadilly line tube 3 days earlier. Though conducted in the relative tranquillity of her back garden, it had been an arduous process. Nearly four hours had passed before they left, taking with them sealed bags containing the soot-covered clothes she'd worn for forensic examination. It had left her feeling shattered but glad. Glad to be of assistance and glad it was all out of the way. Just as she hoped some kind of normality could begin to return to her life, a heavy cough was a spluttered reminder of the smoke and grime she'd inhaled during the long dark walk out of the tunnel.

Though the cough showed little sign of abating her mood had risen with the arrival of bunches of flowers from well-wishers. They stood beautifully arranged in vases.

It was the love and support of friends, colleagues and Jay, her boyfriend that guided her through the tumultuous emotions of shock and anger, numbness and euphoria.

One positive was that she was beginning to be able to feel again. The negative was that now she felt more of a sense of sadness for the victims and those still missing.

A series of images she viewed showed A4 photocopies that had been taped to lampposts and railings around Kings Cross bearing the faces of people who were still missing.

The same faces stared back from her Sunday newspaper, daring her to turn the page without feeling pangs of guilt, berating her morbid curiosity as she sifted through witness accounts of the aftermath, reading and re-reading, gleaning whatever she could from each as Miff, her cat dozed contentedly in the warm sun at her feet.

The feline yawned arched its back, then stood and brushed by her leg, nudging her, bringing her out of the dizzying head spin caused by the strange brew of intrigue and emotion.

As she had on countless occasions since the blast, she thanked her lucky stars, in wonderment at how she'd survived, walking away with just a cut wrist and stitches.

The reflection prompted the inevitable flashback, returning her to where she'd stood a few days before and once again she imagined how many of those in the carriage behind hers must have died in that terrible instant.

The uncertainty wasn't going to go away easily, nor was her constant questioning as to how or *why* anyone would do such a thing to London, her adopted home, a place with so much to give. It was a place with such wonderful diversity and tolerance, a beacon of democracy to people of all shades, cultures and religions the world over.

The 4th Bomb

As Sunday's sun began to lose its warmth Rachel returned inside the flat through the patio doors. On television there was a round-up of the tumultuous week beginning with the Live 8 concerts beamed across the globe on July 2nd. Sir Bob Geldof plucked the public's heartstrings and Chancellor Gordon Brown's pocket in the name of debt and poverty in Africa.

July 6th showed momentous scenes in Singapore where Kelly Holmes and Lord Coe punched the air victoriously.

July 7th showed a sombre announcement from the G8 summit in Gleneagles by Tony Blair who seemed disappointed he was unable to ride the wave of euphoria the Olympic win had brought or been able to make more of the star-studded bash of the previous weekend. Had he delivered the speech days earlier he would have bathed in the saintly glow of Sir Bob and Co, but the days news fell on ears deaf to dark-skinned distant cries. It was eclipsed by screams echoing from blackened choking people closer to home.

Rachel sat down and opened her laptop and began updating the Urban 75 web blog she'd begun on the night of the 7th.

On it she recounted her experiences that day. She had received a large deal of attention from journalists and media wanting details of what happened on the bombed Piccadilly train.

Her blog entry spoke of how it had taken 30 minutes for the stranded survivors to be guided back through the tunnel to safety by transport staff.

After updating her blog she roamed the BBC news site.

She found a diagram illustrating the seat of the explosion located in her tube carriage! The bomb had actually exploded in the carriage *behind* hers. She gasped.

How could such a glaring inaccuracy be made, she asked.

Soon her fingernails, still black with soot began tapping her keyboard in rapid strokes as she typed out an email to the online editor at the BBC.

In the email she recounted many of the details she gave the investigating officers earlier and the newshounds that shoved microphones and cameras in the faces of survivors outside the hospital days before.

Her mobile vibrated and she picked it up, inspecting its screen. She'd been receiving enquiries all weekend from newspapers wanting to send reporters and photographers round.

Neither recognising the number nor relishing the prospect of going through the whole story again, at least not today, she let it divert to voicemail.

She heard a key turn in the lock of the front door.

It was Jay her boyfriend. On entering the room he whipped out a bunch of flowers from behind his back.

'For you!' he announced.

'From Martina and Andy across the road' he added, searching his mind for yet another pot to place them in.

'You're not still on the Internet are you?' he sighed, despairing of his girlfriend's post-traumatic surf disorder.

'Look', she said with a worried expression.

'The BBC news site shows the bomb in the wrong carriage!'

Leaving the flowers on the table Jay turned to her.

'Aw come here' he said with outstretched arms.

The gesture was swiftly reciprocated with a small kiss.

'I'll tell you what... let's go out for a meal.' He said, hoping to take her mind off police statements and BBC balls-ups.

They held each other in an embrace. It was a hug, longer and tighter than usual, as all their hugs had been since Thursday and soon they headed off out the front door hand in hand, walking down the street somewhere in North London.

The 4th Bomb

Daniel's mobile lit up and vibrated against the surface of the glass dining table.

He scooped it up before it could emit its shrill tone.

'Hello... Oh Brian, yeah what's happening?'

'Cheers for last night, really, I apprecia... uh?'

'Christian' Brian repeated starkly.

'Have you seen him...? Everyone's looking for him.'

'Looking for who?' replied Daniel, slightly puzzled.

'Christian.... he didn't return home on Thursday night.'

'Didn't he?' Daniel said realising what Brian was talking about.

'I bumped into him at Euston station on Thursday morning at about... er, five minutes after nine' Daniel replied.

'I'm with his flatmates Vanessa, Simone and Tameka outside University College Hospital right now', Brian said.

'They've been searching for him since Thursday night, sticking up posters and handing out flyers round Kings Cross.'

'Oh' murmured Daniel, taking in the details.

'We're at a complete loss as to what's going on because his car went missing from where he parks it by Walthamstow station where he gets the Victoria line each morning.'

'Hmm, yeeaah I definitely saw him, coming out of Euston Station during the evacuation' said Daniel, summoning up the moment he saw Christian heading off towards the bus stops.

He ruminated further, recalling the previous week when Brian, Christian and himself had hung out in a bar in Ladbroke Grove, as he tried to take in what Brian had told him meant.

'Yeah, Christian passed right by me' Daniel repeated vacantly, as the implication slowly dawned.

'He was in a bit of a hurry like most people were that morning'

'And do you remember what he wore?' Brian asked.

'Yeah, of course'. Such was the friendly but competitive streak among his peers that Daniel recalled feeling a tad underdressed as Christian walked by, even with the benefit of the extra effort and time he'd spent ironing that morning.

'A grey suit with a blue and white shirt and tie.' Daniel replied.
'What are you guys gonna do now?' he asked.
'They're waiting for Christian's mum to come down with some more photos for the newspapers' replied Brian.
'A police liaison officer they spoke to on Thursday night called Gary Jopling took the photos they had of Christian but never contacted them or returned their calls' Brian recounted.
'It turned out he wasn't a liaison officer at all and they're still trying to get their photos of Christian back!'
Daniel listened, fearing the worst.
He seemed trapped, frozen in a kind of limbo, in a daze.
Brian's call ended.
Daniel remembered Christian that morning.
Memories? Were they all that remained? How could it be? Why were things were getting worse, *still*?
He remembered the salsa night the week before when the three of them last met up. The classic funk that gave way to the shrill horns of salsa music and how his fatigued had feet wilted in the heat of competition from Brian's honed meringue technique, how the women lined opposite chatted among each other or exchanged coy introductory smiles with Christian and the other light-footed Latin dancers. *Just the week before.*
Daniel's brainstormed through a raft of slim possibilities and daunting probabilities a number of times.
Christian hadn't reached work on Thursday.
In all honesty what hope was there? His car was gone. How? Taken by whom?
Daniel was left with a host of *what ifs*.
What if? Maybe he couldn't board a bus and made his way back to Walthamstow picking up his car and driving off somewhere… somehow.

II

*Power is nothing
without control*

~Chapter 7~

7 Daze

Londoners resolutely returned to work the following week refusing to be cowed by attacks 'sources' claimed bore all the hallmarks of Al-Qaeda.

Daniel anticipated the week ahead with strangely mixed feelings. As well as his meeting; the thought of which sent a pang of lethargy through him as he woke that morning, today there was a silver lining keeping the stormy outlook at bay.

He left the Prêt-A-Manger on Old Street with a coffee, but today it was the prospect of adding an extra spring to his step that was this morning's perk. Just like a sip of from the grande, it would bring with it the sweet rush of sugar and mocha.

Clasping the warm container he waited for the lift clinging to this thought.

His weekend had been a worrisome one, but today lunchtime would be enjoyable, perhaps even memorable.

With no sign of the fine weather abating they could grab sandwiches and some drinks from Marks & Spencer's and spend lunch relaxing on the green of Finsbury Square.

If only he'd brought a cloth, something to place on the grass for them both to sit or lie back on, he thought dreamily.

Then they could lay beside each other, close their eyes afloat in a dream, drifting off to far away settings, far away from work or worry. To a deserted shore covered with black volcanic sand, perhaps. Anywhere would do, any place where whatever it was he was trying to understand could be understood.

Of course he'd probably need to confirm this with Hilda first he thought, as the muffled clang announcing the lifts arrival brought him back to reality. So much for idle thoughts, but Daniel could've sworn they concurred with a dream he could vaguely recall having sometime over the past few nights.

Hadn't their meeting that day itself been a dream, a fairytale set amid a living nightmare? It had. So maybe his wildest dreams *were* possible, he thought, as the lift began its ascent.

But if his deepest desires *were* real, did they include fanciful whims? He wondered, exiting the lift and entering the office.

No. A whim this was not. Meeting Hilda was *meant* to be, he surmised as he sat at his desk and watched the froth slowly swirl in the cup in front of him.

She was an angel, he could dispense with any pretence.

There was no competition, no need for façades, playing it confident or polite, forward or cocky.

She would follow his lead just like she had that morning.

~

He decided to give her a call after his meeting at eleven. That would give her a chance to settle into her day but leave enough time for her to not decline his invite due to short notice.

Clasping the phone to his ear, he heard the pulse of the dial tone. After a moment's silence a small click sounded as it diverted to voicemail.

'Hmmpf' he muttered, ending the call. It was an inauspicious start to a wondrous union.

Over the next hour he tried her number a few more times but to no avail, it seemed Hilda was otherwise engaged. As noon neared and passed so too did his hopes for lunchtime that day.

Not today then he finally accepted, after the umpteenth attempt. He consoled himself with the fact that he knew there was no need to rush because there had been *something* about their meeting that told him it was just *meant* to be.

Later that afternoon he poked out a jovial sounding text message and sent it to her.

'There.' he said, as a beep confirmed the message had been sent. He had taken his time over it, carefully re-wording it to ensure its tone did not betray the slight disappointment he felt.

He spent the rest of his deskbound lunch on the continued online trail for news surrounding the investigation. Information attributed to 'sources' was certainly adding to the intrigue.

Ashe discarded the packaging from the Marks & Spencer's sandwich he'd eaten he realised he didn't have that much of an appetite for work any more. Concentration was proving difficult. The two paracetamol he washed down with a mouthful of relaxing camomile and honey herbal tea had done little to soothe the dull ache and mental block making his workload seem a Herculean task. Six o'clock couldn't come quickly enough and what was worse was it was only Monday.

~

That evening Daniel entered the subway on Old Street.

He swept past the shops in the underground and passed a flower stall and a man selling copies of The Evening Standard.

The news-stand the vendor stood beside caught Daniel's eye. Its headline read 'Torment Of A Mother'.

Pausing he read the paragraph beside a photograph of a grief stricken women. Her name was Marie Fatayi-Williams.

Tearfully she held aloft a picture of her son Anthony Fatayi-Williams. Daniel recalled seeing him exiting Euston station and heading towards Euston's bus stops that morning.

Tuesday, July 12th

It was already 20 minutes past eight. His movement down the hallway was brisk. He jabbed the lift's call button and waited. Prodding it again he looked up at the illuminated number above the door and shrugged. He didn't have time for this.

Shoving through double doors to the staircase he muttered unspeakables and descended four flights of stairs to the buildings exit.

Being close to the train station was a double-edged sword at times. Once again he'd been lulled into a false sense of time and had been unable to find his keys just as he was supposed to leave for work. Now his watch showed the train was minutes from departure, precipitating a mad dash for the 08:27 Enfield Town to Liverpool Street.

Even if Daniel cared to, he hadn't time to acknowledge Kieran. He ignored the security manager whose head nosed around the management office door.

The reticence of both men reflected a low point that had been reached, where even a polite greeting would have been two-faced. Already late and with more pressing issues Daniel kept walking, not wishing to burden himself further with minor concerns but half way down the road he couldn't resist a glance over his shoulder.

Yeah, he could have guessed it.

Kieran had come outside and was following his progress down the road. He was standing at the top of the stairs with his mobile clasped to his ear.

What does he want? Thought Daniel angrily, as he continued down the road to the station.

He arrived at work surprised to find a near empty office. Perhaps the threat of being blown-up by Al Qaeda still acting loomed large, he thought looking around.

Ron, the senior manager was absent and Brendan was on holiday. That made things a bit more flexible Daniel supposed, and with so many absent the office had a light air about.

As he sat down he got the feeling that this was going to be a low output day, a low output week even.

Across the open plan office was Dan Straw, the I.T Manager who sat hunched over his monitor. Tariq hurried off to a meeting while James and Dave sat manning their workstations. From looking at the I.T support desk he could tell Patrick was busy somewhere and in the corner sat Ainsworth, chuckling madly at his monitor, as if watching his minion's preparations for world domination taking shape.

Daniel logged onto his machine and decided he would focus on planning today rather than doing, after all he did have to take things easy.

There was the Post Traumatic Stress he was warned could manifest at some point, in a form that was as yet unclear.

Some time after eleven, Oliviere walked in. He extracted his laptop from its case and placed it on the desk opposite Daniel.

'Pub lunch anyone?' Enquired James, loudly enough for all in earshot to look up from their monitor's as the Frenchman removed his jacket. A round of chuckles reverberated and Oliviere accepted the banter with an easy smile.

Daniel prodded his keyboard aimlessly and restricted his mirth to a gleeful smirk as he flicked from news site to news site.

Osama drama here, Al-Zarqawi malarkey there, the war on terror raged and the minutes before noon in a grey office block on the corner of Old Street ticked slowly by.

'Er... Hello... Hilda? It's Daniel' he said, trying Hilda's number again and being caught by surprise when she'd actually answered.

'Yeah I'm okay... how've you been?'

'Didn't you get my text message?' he asked.

'Oh... okay then' he replied.

'So you'll be back at work tomorrow then?'

'Alright, make sure you text me your email address, okay?'

The conversation ended. And that was it.

Yess! He thought. He'd made contact. It was a breakthrough no matter how brief it was. He got up and left the office satisfied with his mornings work, daydreaming as he waited for the lift.

Outside the building a few nicotine users stood puffing on cigarettes. Two policemen in florescent high-visibility jackets were posted nearby, dutifully keeping an eye out for lurking terror. Behind them Daniel slipped on his shades and turned the corner at a leisurely pace, in no hurry to return to the office as the rays of warm sun on his face cleared his congested mind. A little way down City Road he passed the Honourable Artillery Company barracks. Its security had been beefed-up since Friday, when he'd stopped to allow a procession of lorries turning from the main road to enter its gates.

Now a large acetate sheet similar to those that surrounded forensic crime scenes shrouded its entrance, barrier and gatehouse where a lone security guard was normally stationed. On his way back from Marks & Spencer's there were six uniformed policemen standing outside it. One stepped forward as he approached.

'There he is' the officer sneered to his colleagues, who all turned observing Daniel as he approached.

He passed them, unable to clearly hear whatever disparaging remarks they'd exchanged and were sniggering about.

'Hey Dan, I was walking past the old army barracks on City Road...'

'Er... yeah' answered Dan, still peering into his monitor.

'I was just wondering... *what goes on in there*?' Daniel asked.

Dan Straw swivelled round in his chair, scratching his head.

His furrowed brow gave his face the permanent look of worry he always seemed to have that belied his T-shirt and jeans approach to office attire.

'Um, yeah' he began, after consulting his memory.

'If I'm not mistaken it's an old military base that formerly housed mercenaries for hire by the crown.'

'But more recently the City of London Police are associated with it... they're using it as a temporary morgue'

'Really?' said Daniel, his interest aroused.

'Yeah, to house the victims from last week's attacks', he added.

Hmm, Daniel thought. *A morgue*. So that's what those vans he saw last Friday were delivering... *bodies*.

He began to wonder what was wrong with the many regular morgues around London? Aren't bodies normally held at a local infirmary with laboratories and forensic science facilities, he thought, as he sliced into his salmon and pasta salad.

Was the departure from standard procedure for any particular reason? He wondered. There must be a reason for this change to have been made.

He sipped from what appeared to be an upmarket brand of fruit juice. In fact it was a mini-bottle of Chardonnay he felt would be more refreshing than herbal tea and slightly more effective than the paracetamol he gulped down with water earlier. He looked up at the office monitor showing the latest news update on the investigation. It featured footage from a statement from Deputy Assistant Commissioner Peter Clarke, who, it turns out just *also* happened to be head of the *Anti-Terror Branch* at Scotland Yard. He had given a progress report at a press conference earlier that morning.

Text transcript taken at a press briefing held on the 12th July 2005
Venue: Queen Elizabeth II Centre, London

'It is now nearly a week since more than 50 people were murdered and several hundred injured in an appalling terrorist attack here in London.

From that moment on, as the Commissioner declared last week, police have worked painstakingly to put together every shred of evidence we could to mount what we want to be a successful investigation.

Several hundred witness statements have already been taken, over 1000 actions have been raised, many of them prompted by some very useful and constructive calls from the public to our anti-terrorist hotline.'

Deputy Assistant Commissioner Peter Clarke

Several hundred witness statements. That got Daniel wondering.
How important was the information he had to the investigation? And when would someone from the army of detectives D.A.C Peter Clarke said were making solid headway in the investigation, contact him? Six days had passed.

He had already contacted the police *twice* with no response. Given the gravity of the matter this was curious.

Daniel could sense that something was not right and somehow it was connected to his fears about Christian's whereabouts and the even stranger disappearance of his car.

One thing the delay had done was allow him time to get a grip on himself and make sense of what he saw outside the numbed state of shock. He had been hesitant as he stood outside the police station the day after in a bid to make a police statement. Even now he still felt uncomfortable commenting on anything, as the media version of events seemed to be evolving.

Daniel boarded the Northern line train at Old Street that evening listening to an MP3 playlist he'd created. It was a laidback selection of tracks intended to keep his mind off things.

Opening with 'Sailing' By Christopher Cross, the sound was almost drowned out by the noise of the tube hurtling through London's underbelly.

Daniel pressed the earphones firmly into his ears in a bid to transport himself to a more secluded place, far from the rush hour crush and post-traumatic jitters.

Two stops on he caught the Victoria line from Kings Cross to Seven Sisters. Earth, Wind and Fire's 'You Can't Hide' played.

By the time the haunting intro of the definitive version of 'People Make The World Go Round' by The Stylistics began, he felt a burning sensation in the back of his neck. Daniel turned and there facing him was a man standing by the tube doors.

He was in his early 40's, navy blue jacket, denim trousers with a black rucksack slung over one shoulder. Their gazes met and looked away at precisely the same moment.

Moments later Daniel scrutinised the man again, this time more closely noting his demeanor.

His dark hair was receding at the sides but the hair on top was thicker and combed over to cover the shortcomings. Daniel was sure he recalled seeing this man somewhere before, but where? The man's gaze had retreated to staring downwards when the doors opened. He immediately got off and walked down the platform, but not before Daniel had taken a snap of him on his camera-phone as he waited for the tube's doors to slide open. As the train pulled away Daniel wondered. It could've been anyone he supposed, doubting himself for a moment. Forget it, he decided, trying to not too dwell on it too much. He saved the snap he took and pressed play on his phone's Mp3 player.

The next track was '7 Years Good Luck' by Joe Sample.

Wednesday, July 13th

Before leaving for work he took a detour to the basement.

He turned a small key in his mailbox, lifted the flap and was reaching inside, when right on cue Kieran Watson arrived down the stairs watching him.

'Whatchulookinat?' Daniel spat, throwing him a furious glare.

Kieran smiled glibly, rattling the bunch of keys attached to his waist and slunk off through the exit to the car park.

Daniel retrieved his mail and followed the security manager as he returned through the car park upstairs to the concierge desk in the entrance. There he sat behind a bank of CCTV monitors.

Kieran's prying had become more and more intrusive of recent. Daniel first noticed Kieran taking a keen interest in his business when some of his tittle-tattle came to his attention via his retired neighbour Vera from down the hallway.

Daniel had disregarded it at first but it was becoming clear that it was not as innocuous as he'd imagined.

Exiting the car park he left for the station thinking back to the earliest incidence of Kieran taking more than a passing interest in his comings and goings. Their first encounter was in a local bar when Kieran first started his job.

They politely shared idle chat over the chink of a few beers. Kieran said he was in his early 40's and mentioned something about having 2 kids, *somewhere*. He didn't care to elaborate.

He supposed Kieran's kids were his own responsibility, but it marked him out as someone who was undependable.

Later on, what made him give Kieran a wide berth was his transparent attempts at trying to befriend him to rent his spare room, even though he could tell Kieran didn't even like him.

That immediately gave Daniel the sense that Kieran had a darker motive beyond just being *faux* chummy and hanging around the pubs and bars of Enfield Town eyeing-up skirt.

Daniel approached the train station mildly concerned about a group of uniformed police outside its entrance.

Today he had a small diary and pen with him to take notes should there be any more peculiar sightings or goings on.

The number of police vans present made him wonder if there was background chatter of further attacks?

As he passed by he tried to eavesdrop the uniformed cops nattering among themselves as he entered the station.

Travelling to and from work was getting a bit tense of late. Maybe he would try a different route tomorrow.

~

'Yes!' Daniel hissed, triumphantly. There, in his inbox was a reply to the email he sent Hilda and her response said they could meet at lunchtime on Friday!

Great, he thought, leaning back in his seat.

How long it had been since he'd seen her? It was just a week, but it felt like much longer. It was strange though.

In that time he'd had no contact from the investigators, just a few odd encounters that were beginning to stoke unsettling scenarios in the recesses of his mind.

Seeing the number of other survivor accounts that had been published in the press had got him thinking it might be a good idea to get his account out there.

But which type of publication should he approach?

A conservative rant-rag or a right-leaning titillating tabloid?

Either way, could he be certain he would receive unadulterated coverage? The British media is tightly controlled by the M.O.D, even though they like the little people to believe their press is the yardstick of the 'free world'. His story could easily be misconstrued, even his name questioned. Regardless he knew he *had* to establish the fact that he was on the bus, *somehow*.

On his way to lunch that afternoon Daniel stopped at a mobile phone shop. He paid £30 cash for a budget handset with a new network Sim-card.

He took the measure of paying by cash to ensure it could not be traced to him and his calls monitored, at least not initially. Once he was back at the office he used it to ring The Daily Mail's news-desk entering 141 to hide his caller-id.

A young woman answered. After a few reticent responses to the questions she posed him, she began huffing, insisting he explain precisely what his story entailed.

So she'd had a bad experience with crankster's in the past.

Daniel certainly wasn't going to blurt what he knew out over the telephone and get a 6-line entry on page 29, column 5.

This was the stuff of *major* scoops, exclusives, front pages and double-page spreads in the area of *serious* investigative journalism. He hung up and tried the next number on his list, but soon found that all his calls met with a similar impasse.

~

Late that afternoon he stood in the hallway and tried again. This time he tried calling a list of Sunday papers. The dial tone throbbed. He could see it. A major scoop in the News of the World or The Sunday Mirror, an eyewitness exclusive!

To his surprise the receptionist who picked up put him straight though to the news-desk without so much as a hello who are you, where an eager newshound took a few notes and arranged a meeting with him that very evening. It was on!

Amazing. He had arranged to meet a journalist from the Sunday Mirror at 7pm in front of Liverpool Street station.

Now that wasn't so bad, Daniel thought, as he headed back to the office, wondering how it all was going to pan out.

That afternoon he dashed home, changed clothes and emerged minutes later in a tracksuit and trainers.

He returned to the train station warily glancing around at the CCTV cameras on the empty platform.

On catching his reflection in a panel of the waiting area on the platform he wondered if his attire or apprehensive demeanour was drawing attention to himself.

His sweater's collar was zipped right up to his chin and his tracksuit top's hood was up despite the sun's warmth.

Beneath it his black baseball cap was pulled down low, making eye contact optional.

After some time a shrill warbling tone rang out. He dug around in his back pocket and retrieved the small handset he bought earlier that day.

'Hello?' he answered cautiously.

'Yeah, I'm still coming', he said, eyeing an approaching train.

'I'll be about 20 minutes late' he told the caller.

'Yes, in front of the station. I'll see you then' Daniel replied, knowing he had no intention of meeting the journalist there.

~

Approximately 35 minutes later he got off the train and made his way out of Liverpool Street station down a side road.

He stopped at a brassiere and sat at one of seats outside and peered out over a copy of The Metro newspaper he found lying on the table.

A svelte eastern European waitress came out and buffed the table top down, her smile beamed at him as if from a parallel universe where the *War on Terror* was a laughable concept.

Daniel raised a weak smile in return and feigned interest in the a la carte menu she placed in front of him.

His concerns were beginning to grow about two police vans that had just parked down the street when his phone chirped again.

'Yes, I'm there, where are you?' Daniel asked, folding the paper and looking out towards the high road.

'Where we arranged, in front of the station' said the voice.

'Okay, go inside and come out of the station's east entrance' Daniel instructed.

'I'm outside a, er... coffee shop just across the road' he said.

As soon as he ended the call Daniel stood up and crossed back over to Liverpool Street stations side entrance and sat at a table outside the McDonalds restaurant scanning his surroundings. He looked at his watch. It was 7:33pm.

A man with a sports holdall hovered at the top of the elevator that lead up from the station's concourse.

Daniel redialled the last number on his phone.

The man responded, reaching into his shirt pocket and flipping out a mobile phone.

'Hello, where are you?' the voice asked.

The man appeared to be on his own, but Daniel still got up and retreated into the restaurant taking a seat by the window.

'Look to your left...' Daniel directed.

'Inside McDonald's'

The shaven-headed male turned towards the restaurant and stood in its entrance taking a cursory glance around the busy dining area. He spotted where Daniel was and walked over and sat in the chair opposite him.

'Hi... Michael Duffy' he offered, thrusting a hand towards the shrouded figure.

Daniel adjusted the rim of his baseball cap upwards meeting his steely greyish stare. His jaw-line bore the merest hint of 4 o'clock shadow, his shirt's top button was undone and he'd loosened his tie. Daniel held out a cautious hand.

Duffy quickly flashed what looked like an ID card of some sort. He felt this was sufficient proof of his credentials as he placed a notepad on the table and began his questioning.

'So... you were aboard the bus?' he began, speaking with a slight antipodean twang or possibly a hint of a white Southern Afrikaans accent.

'Yes, I was' came the response.

'That must've been a horrendous experience!' Duffy said, raising his eyebrows in a manner indicating concern.

Daniel was more concerned with the open Adidas holdall that sat open on the floor beside the journalist. His eye wandered over its exterior wondering what was in its interior.

Some kind of microphone or a recorder perhaps?

He could only imagine what the bag of tricks contained.

Daniel leant back in his chair and lowered his tone.

'Aren't you gonna ask me for some proof of ID?' Daniel asked surprised by the briskness and informality of his major scoop.

'After all, I could be anyone' he reasoned, lowering the brim of his cap further down about his head.

Duffy placed his pen down and clasping his hands together like a man of the cloth, he leant forward and spoke, lowering his voice as if passing information in the strictest of confidence.

'What I want to do Daniel, is know if you'd be willing to do an interview for an article and maybe take a photo to go with it?''

After mulling over Duffy's offer for a moment, Daniel rubbed his chin and made a few conciliatory sounds. He didn't really trust the guy. This article had to be done properly or not at all.

'Erm, I'll pass on the photograph' he replied politely.

His momentary dithering had raised a glint in Duffy's eye, which then dimmed to a look of disappointment when his offer was declined, but a moment later Duffy tried a different tact.

He dipped into his holdall and took out a brown envelope. From it he produced a photograph of a young Asian male and placed it on the table.

'Did you see this man on the bus at any time?' Duffy asked, swivelling it round for the interviewee's perusal.

'Did… I… see… him?' said Daniel repeating Duffy's words slowly. He examined the picture closely, looking long and hard at the face in the photograph, searching his memory.

Daniel glanced up and saw the hack watching him intently as he scrutinised the image.

He returned his focus to the picture and closed his eyes. He retraced his meandering path through Euston's main hall towards W.H Smiths where he briefly looked at the covers of a few PC magazines before leaving to linger outside the station, watching people head for taxi-ranks and bus stops.

'No… I didn't' came his response. Daniel's hand slid the photo back across the table towards Duffy.

His response didn't seem to register with the journalist.

'I never saw him on the bus' Daniel repeated with finality and he leant back in the moulded plastic seating for a moment before realising how ridiculously uncomfortable it was.

'Are you certain? *Think*! Search your memory!' Duffy urged.

'Are you *really* sure?' he asked, giving Daniel the impression that he wanted him to finger the young Asian anyway.

'Course I'm sure. I was the 4th or 5th person to board the bus when it arrived at Euston. I stood on the lower deck the whole time.' Duffy continued tapping his pen impatiently, as if he'd yet to hear anything of interest.

'Most of the people boarding would have brushed past me.'

Daniel reeled of other bits about what happened after the explosion, but none of this seemed to be of interest to Duffy.

He wanted the young Asian in the picture to be identified as being aboard the bus.

The glint Duffy had in his eye on shaking hands earlier was no longer in evidence. He laid his pen down on the table.

It was obvious to Daniel that he wasn't too concerned with any details of what he had to say.

'When will the article be published?' chirped Daniel hopefully, as Duffy glanced at his watch a second time.

'Er, here's my card… call me you if you remember anything else about the guy in the picture.' He replied.

Hmm… okay, Daniel nodded examining the card Duffy handed him. Duffy lent over and picked up his Adidas holdall. He then stood-up and left. Daniel watched him, mulling over the offer he'd turned down. He had been given a clear choice. Either he identified the young Asian in the photo as being on the bus to get the newspaper article or else no article at all.

Back to square one then he figured, neatly depositing Duffy's card in a litterbin outside the station.

Establishing that he was on the bus still remained a priority.

Thursday, July 14th

The radio launched into a flurry of minor delays, lane closures and tailbacks before returning to its usual rambling formula of topical chat. A yawn followed what had been a restless night.

Daniel's arm swung across, feeling for, then pressing a button on the radio alarm clock to negotiate a few extra minutes rest for the day ahead.

Forty minutes later he swept down the back staircase to the ground floor and along a passage to a fire exit in a bid to avoid the CCTV cameras covering the blocks exits and entrances.

If Kieran was at his post he had to assume they were all being monitored. He let himself out through a rear fire exit.

After waiting by a hedgerow on the corner of the road, he dashed across the road to the bus stop, signalling with an outstretched arm to the driver of a double-decker approaching from Enfield Town centre. He boarded the sparsely populated bus and sat downstairs at the rear.

Of three possible routes he could have taken to work, this was the one he only took if the trains were cancelled.

The bus accelerated through the leafy outskirts of North London heading towards Wood Green. From there he would catch the Piccadilly line underground to work.

As it sped along Daniel stifled another yawn and rested his head against the window grabbing a moments rest. Suddenly a loud thud startled him, jolting him to his senses, he looked round, expecting to find an object had struck the bus window. His face was met with the snarling grimace of a man gripping the steering wheel of a white van driving alongside. Shattered fragments of what remained of the van's mirror dangled wildly in the wind as the driver gritted his teeth menacingly.

'Wanker!' Daniel mouthed, pressing a middle finger against the window at the driver whose grimace contorted into a furious glare. Daniel snapped back into his seat out of view as the bus surged ahead. The van driver responded, accelerating further up alongside the bus, driving insanely close at speed.

This continued all the way down Green Lanes till just as quickly as it had begun, it was over. The white van accelerated ahead with a sudden burst of speed, nipping in front of the bus, just before the road narrowed up ahead. The look of absolute hatred in the van driver's face as he sped past told Daniel that the man expected him to *fear* them. All it did was leave Daniel wondering what the significance of it was.

Okay, it'd confirmed one thing. The suspicions he'd had. Suspicions that he was under round-the-clock surveillance.

But why was that necessary and did it mean he was being watched wherever he went?

Mercifully, the underground station was only a minute's walk from the bus stop at Wood Green and Daniel disappeared along with the torrent of commuters into Wood Green underground's depths, pondering the dimension the chase added to his predicament.

The 4th Bomb

A week on from the event that had begun the flashbacks now haunting his resting and waking thoughts, Daniel was given further opportunity to remember. It was just before midday. The office began emptying and he joined the flow of people down six flights of stairs, assembling in the street outside.

Soon hundreds had gathered among the tall buildings around Old Street, one of London's busiest thoroughfares. Office staff, creative workers, city workers and staff from nearby coffee shops had brought its persistent flow to a complete standstill.

A hushed silence fell as vehicle engines were turned off.

Side-by-side, Londoner's stood motionless to observe the 2 minute silence in remembrance of the bombing victims.

Though all of London was united in grief Daniel felt apart from the many religions, classes and races that stood silently.

He thought of his friend, Christian *Njoya Diawara* Small.

A week on and still no one knew where Christian was. Was he alive or dead? When would the investigators contact him? What would he tell them? Too many questions remained unanswered.

He knew that somewhere behind the impassioned speeches, beneath the veneer of unity lay a darker agenda, one that in time would explain why he was being watched and trailed.

But for now he tapped his feet impatiently.

The two-minute silence became unbearable. It was an empty façade, disgusting him. Injustice disgusted him and he felt disgusted with himself for standing there, going along with it. A fake show of unity was a photo opportunity for sombre faced politicians to posture on cue, as dark powers sowed deeper divisions in this 'harmonious' society we call London.

The question that had pressed Daniel for the whole 2 minutes fought for resolution. Was he a suspect? *Why*? And if he was, why didn't they just question him like any other survivor?

What did they hoped to achieve with surveillance? And when would it end? How would it end?

After work that day he entered the subway and approached the central foyer of Old Street underground.

He couldn't fail to notice a lingering stare from a man.

The man's hand smoothed the greying streaks of hair on one side of his shaven-head as he turned away in a gesture that failed to make him appear less conspicuous.

Worn jeans and trainers on a man in his 40's, loitering in an underground, as all around him commuters scurried to catch trains home, may have given the uninitiated the impression he was in the early stages of vagrancy, but Daniel knew otherwise. He wasn't loitering. He'd been stationed there and from the look on his face seemed to be attempting to gauge Daniel's reaction to the headline on an awkwardly re-positioned newspaper stand.

Its poster heralded the unveiling of *the bus bomber*.

What do they think they're playing at? Daniel thought.

A small smile of realisation slowly set on his face. He was certain he recognised the man from somewhere, but where?

Wait-a-minute… that was it! The man in the dark MPV he encountered on a morning jog last weekend!

Daniel swept past the man standing by a pile of newspapers. They featured the face of a young Asian male. It was the exact *same* photo shown to him by Michael Duffy the previous day.

Face Of A Suicide Bomber read the paper's headline.

Through the ticket barriers and down the elevator Daniel went, trying to guess what a Sunday paper journalist was doing with a picture that hadn't been released to the public *on Wednesday*?

He could be working for someone else, but whether Duffy did or didn't, Daniel knew he'd been right to trust his instincts that day, giving Duffy nothing of what he really saw that day.

Friday, July 15th

Thank God it was Friday. The working week was almost over and his much-anticipated date with Hilda was this afternoon.

He'd thought about Hilda a lot over the past week, spending what seemed like hours daydreaming about her, but it got him through. *She* got him through. She was like an angel.

She must have been heaven sent, a god-send.

It was re-assuring to know there was someone out there who could relate to what he'd been through, and it was someone he felt he could easily become affectionate towards.

The snarling buzz of the electronic blinds rotating in response to the light stirred him. Their parting allowed light to stream in, coaxing him out of his slumber.

Daniel arose and spun the knob in the en-suite bathroom.

After a hot shower he rubbed dry an area in the bathrooms steamed-up mirror and peered through, inspecting the whites of his brushed teeth. The supple lines of his frame were summarily inspected as cocoa butter was applied to his skin.

Tonight, he thought, rubbing a splash of Davidoff Cool Water into his neck. That should do, he thought, before pulling on his clothes, fragrant and fresh for the day ahead.

At work a pang of dread shot through him as he scanned the subject line of an email in his inbox.

Warily he clicked on it, zooming in on the gist of its content.

It seemed his lunch-date with Hilda would not materialise after all. Something about a meeting over-running and a heavy workload due to her week starting midday on Wednesday.

He was about to descend into a strop when a wave of relief flooded over him as he reading the last lines of her email.

Thank God! Daniel thought, breathing easily once more.

She said they could meet *after* work if it was fine by him.

Fine? It was even better! Now they could get reacquainted without the constraint of time precipitating a mad dash back to the office.

Daniel let out a sigh of relief. Maybe it'll be all right, he told himself. This week everything seemed to keep getting worse, but hopefully things would begin to change for the better. Wasn't this the tumultuous nature of change itself?

At 6.50pm he cleared his desk, shutdown his workstation and took the stairs. This would allow him to carry out a final appearance check in the men's restroom on the 3rd floor.

Outside he crossed City Road and headed down to Finsbury Square, scrolling through the contacts in his phone.

He sent Hilda a quick text reminding her he was on his way. At Finsbury Square he stood around for a while, watching a few stragglers still sitting on patches of yellowing grass as the sun dipped.

The time was 7.25pm. She was nearly half an hour late.

Give her time, he told himself, all the time she needs, he thought, determined nothing should foul up their date.

At 7.32pm he popped one of the Extra Mints he bought from the newsagent's across the road and tried her number again.

'Hello. It's Daniel… where are you?'

'Oh, hi babes… I'm just leaving the office now' she said.

'When do you think you'll get here?' Daniel asked.

'Er, soon… I'm walking up towards you now' Hilda replied.

Daniel could hear the filtered bustle of transport swishing by in his earpiece. He looked out down City Road seeing nothing matching her slender form on the horizon.

He looked again. A man in a brown leather jacket paced by.
A couple frolicked on a bench outside a bar across the street.
A white van thundered away from a set of traffic lights.

'I'm almost there'

'Where are you?' she said.

Daniel didn't understand, there was no sign of her.

'I'm literally standing on the green of Finsbury Square, like we arranged' he said in a slightly agitated tone, as the feeling that something might yet go awry began to grow.

'Describe a road or building nearby'? He asked.

'Well there's a small road and a sign with a map' Hilda replied.

'I'm walking up to its gates'

'How far is it from Moorgate tube station?' Daniel asked.

'Er, about 4, 5 minutes away?' she estimated.

'Oh… I'm on Finsbury Square, your near Finsbury green!'

'I think you got confused' he chuckled.

'I'll start walking down to you.'

'I think *you* got confused more like' Hilda retorted, laughing.

'Hey, I've only worked around here for 6 weeks!' He said.

'You've worked round here for 4 years, you should've told me there was more than one grass area!

Was that her he could see up ahead? Yes. There she was, approaching with her bag slung over her shoulder.

As he drew nearer he noticed her smile.

They hugged and Daniel planted the side of his plump lips on both her cheeks and looked upon her again, re-familiarising himself with her.

'Well… Hilda', he said, as though not quite believing his eyes.

'You made it, finally. How are things? How was your day?'

'I mean, *forget* work, how've you been?' he said, nearly engaging geek mode.

'More important is where are we gonna go?' he enthused.

'Er… to a nice bar, for drinks?' suggested Hilda with a smile.

'Then we can get a bite to eat maybe?' He said, as they set off.

The conversation continued as they left Moorgate heading into the heart of London's financial district, arriving at Bank.

'Well, it depends what kind of food you like' Daniel said.

'I dunno… Thai, Italian maybe…' Hilda replied.

'We could try Nigerian food?' He suggested.

'Goat-meat pepper soup? Pounded yam with ogbonna soup washed down with Nigerian Guinness stout?'

Hilda looked at him like he was a madman and they both burst out laughing.

The bar they entered was packed with a casually dressed after work crowd. Euphoric house music played in the background.

Daniel waded among the throng piled deep at the bar waiting to be served.

After a long wait he asked for a Long Island iced tea then ordered a vodka and orange and a medium white wine.

Sipping the cocktail he watched the barman preparing the vodka and kept an eye on where Hilda was, should one of the smiling guys they passed standing near the entrance get any ideas in his extended absence.

By the time he returned with the drinks the lights had dimmed. Flashes from spotlights glinted in his eye, colored lights flickered, changing colour in unison as the pulsating music grew louder.

He handed the drink to Hilda, barely able to hear her reply. The music was so loud he just nodded, agreeing with whatever it was she said. She promptly turned round and went outside. Daniel's eyes followed her.

She took out her mobile phone and proceeded to make a call.

He turned away and watched some of the drinkers waving about on the dance-floor as the pub they'd entered completed its transformation into a nightclub.

Not the ideal place to get better acquainted in, he thought.

'The bars around here aren't all that on a Friday', Daniel said, as the both peered in the window of a second venue.

'Nah, not like on a Thursday' Hilda agreed.

'I suppose for most finance-sector types its straight back home to wifey dearest come Friday. To some place with *shire* on the end' he explained. Not like us Londoners', he chuckled.

He saw Hilda's lips pull into a smirk. He offered her his arm and the search for a less cacophonous establishment continued.

'It's here somewhere' Hilda assured him a short time later.

They had walked a while before crossing the road towards a building that had no recognisable entrance.

She led him through a doorway and down a staircase with walls decorated with ornate woodcuttings of eastern figures. The floor was covered in a deep red carpet that led into a cavernous dining area where a young oriental lady appeared greeting them with a smile.

The lady silently gestured and showed them through the sparsely populated restaurant to a table.

The scarlet décor continued in the detailing of the dining areas sumptuous curtains and dark wood panelling.

Subdued lighting dimmed an intimate corner.

There they sat side by side on the comfy seating as eastern strings washed gently in the background.

'Nice place' said Daniel, nodding agreeably.

'Yeah... more my kind of thing', Hilda said.

'And *more* intimate' she added, with a flirtatious smile.

She took a lighter from her bag and lit the cigarette she'd slotted between her lips. Daniel stared at the list of wines and reminded himself not to get his hopes up too high.

The drinks menu didn't hold the key to unravelling Hilda's playfulness or the teasing sheer black blouse she chose to wear, but maybe a bottle of wine or two might help.

After a short while the oriental lady reappeared with two taller menus and a complimentarily bowl of spiced prawn crackers.

'Let's share a bottle of red?' Daniel suggested.

'Er… I'll just have a glass of medium white' Hilda replied.

'Okay, maybe I'll get a bottle anyway' he said perusing the list.

'Can I try that one, the Rioja?' He said pointing at the wine list.

'I want something red and medium bodied? Slightly fruity.'

The lady nodded several more times than was necessary, as if the wine would become whatever he desired.

'And a glass of medium dry white wine please' said Hilda.

'Oh, and can we have another bowl of prawn crackers!' Daniel called out after her. She turned and duly nodded.

'That's your meal sorted then' he quipped, crunching on the fast disappearing crackers.

When the wine arrived Daniel took a sip under the watchful gaze of the waitress who attentively awaited his verdict.

Medium bodied? The stuff was thicker than diesel. He coughed, clearing his throat and wondered if she would be so serene if he asked her to take the bottle away?'

'Here, what do you think of this?' he said, holding out the glass to Hilda. Hilda refused drawing her head back.

'Go on, just try it' he urged.

'No… I can't', she said more emphatically.

'Huh? Oh all right then' he said, nodding to the attentive lady who placed the bottle on the table and left silently.

'But remember, I'm not responsible for anything that happens after I drink the whole bottle myself!' he chuckled, quaffing the remainder.

'So what's going on this weekend?' Daniel asked as he continued on the prawn crackers.

'Quite a few things actually, Hilda replied.

'There's two barbecue's on Saturday and the country fair in Brockwell Park on Sunday'

'Really? I'll be in South London on Sunday' Daniel said.

'Will you? Brockwell Park's near where I live' said Hilda.

'Maybe we could meet up? I know the area' Daniel said.

'My family use to live there back in the seventies and I lived in Brixton not far from there myself in the nineties' he said.

'What's it like there nowadays? He asked, pouring more wine.

'Uh, it's okay I suppose' Hilda sighed.

'It was getting hectic when I lived there, that's why I moved out in the end'.

He felt Hilda's thigh against his. He felt so at ease next to her. As the wine disappeared so too had some of his inhibitions.

He placed a hand on her thigh and chuckled. Hilda threw him a look. Her hand came down and clasped firmly on top of his.

He chuckled some more. The image of an angel he'd built-up from afar had come down to earth. She was just like he was, guarded, with an air of unpredictability about her.

'Hey, what's your star sign?' he asked.

Later they emerged from the Thai restaurant, the sky had turned a deep azure blue. The time was way past tipsy.

The city had emptied. They had the whole financial district to themselves. They were the last pedestrians, the last survivors.

Daniel was beginning to think he might regret consuming a whole bottle of wine as an illuminated blurry London stood before them. After a few strides he stopped and turned to Hilda. He felt the warmth of her embrace. It felt like sanctuary.

'Ooh, I missed you too!' she cooed, saying what he'd been trying to say for the last few hours, few days... week.

He leant forward and his lips touched hers.

His hands slid down the curve of her back to her waist coming to a rest on her hips. His touch was gentle but firm, firm enough to make it clear that any resistance was a futile endeavour, firm enough to indicate that despite the hesitancy the past week had instilled in him, he was a powerful man who's feelings could not be taken lightly.

'Feelin' frisky are we?' Hilda enquired, with a wry smile.

'A bit sloshed too' he replied, with a mischievous grin.

Hilda giggled.

'That felt good' he said.

'There's more where that came from' teased Hilda.

His hold on her tightened. He planted another kiss on her lips. This time it lingered, lasting till the drone of a lone motorcycle in the distance grew to a crescendo and tore past them, fading to nothing as they turned for the station.

Arm in arm they entered the warm snugness of the underground station. Daniel felt a warm feeling inside as they waited for a Northern line train to arrive.

When the train they boarded reached Hilda's stop they parted company as they had begun, with a peck on both cheeks.

Only the tube packed with drinkers on their way in and revellers on their way out prevented him taking things further. And he couldn't have cared less about who was observing him.

~Chapter 8~

Man Of Great Spirit

Fragments of a pleasant dream he couldn't quite recall the precise details of, dissipated as he stirred.

He'd woken up alone but no longer felt solitude, instead he felt something between the excitement of a child eagerly looking forward to a school trip and the guarded resolve of a man, cautiously holding back a deluge of pent-up emotion.

It was almost noon, he needed to get up and start getting ready. He'd spent all of Saturday thinking about today, because today his social itinerary was at full capacity.

He closed his eyes and envisaged what he would wear as he dozed a while longer. A white short-sleeved shirt from Zara For Men, a pair of three-quarter length khaki shorts, some tan coloured soft leather slip-on loafers and the tour de force; a straw panama hat, keeping the sun's rays off his head while providing an understated air of seasonal sophistication.

Tilted at just the right angle it was perfect for a laid back Sunday afternoon.

First there was the gathering at the Black Cultural Archives in Brixton, South London. It had been convened in one of the flurry of emails exchanged during the frantic weeklong search for news concerning Christian's whereabouts.

As this question remained unanswered, the gathering was not for people to show their condolences, it was a vigil, providing an opportunity for his friends to come together and show support during what was a harrowing period of uncertainty for his family.

Daniel stared up at the ceiling above wondering what the tone of proceedings would be. It would not be a good idea to utter a word of what he knew to anyone there, as having seen

Christian that morning in Euston he'd already accepted the only logical explanation for his disappearance. It had resonated as soon he received the phone call from Brian last Sunday telling of their friend's disappearance.

Still, if people clung to a glimmer of hope, no matter how tiny, he would suspend the inescapable dread for as long as an unclear picture remained.

It must be terrible being left hanging like that, Daniel thought, wondering what Christian's family were going through.

He could hardly believe what *he* was going through, with spooks watching and shady characters trailing him. He had a lot on his mind. Maybe Hilda was the only thing preventing his fraying nerves from sliding into a post-traumatic state.

That was why he had reason to be thankful. She had proven what was most important, someone *understanding him.*

Of course, his family thanked God he survived on his return home, but were unable to grasp what had happened and couldn't understand why everything hadn't just returned back to normal after he returned to work after the attacks.

Mercifully he had something more. He had *Hilda,* someone who'd been right there with him, guiding him through it!

She'd agreed to meet him on the corner of Coldharbour lane at 5:30pm. It was a short walk from the Cultural Archives, not far from where she said she lived, so his day mapped out perfectly. His need for social interaction would be satiated.

They could spend the rest of the afternoon in Brockwell Park at the country fair, relaxing with a picnic, listening to the sound systems as they watched the crowds go by.

He dragged himself out of bed, showered and got dressed.

After a quick bowl of cereal, he stood in front of the mirror paying meticulous attention to the lean of his hat, as a few degrees either way could mean the difference between debonair and derisory. Once satisfied, he set off on his way to south London.

The 4th Bomb

Brixton underground station was teeming with as much character as any of the busy markets the area was renown for. People enjoying their weekend filed through, infected by the lively buzz of an area reflective of its large Caribbean and African community.

Back on his old stomping ground Daniel ascended the steps. Today the station's welcoming committee of assorted loiterers and street characters had been deterred by an increased police presence, two of whom were detaining a regular who'd been trying to resell used travel passes. Daniel swerved past the police interrogation and climbed the stairs up to street level.

Outside the station he turned right passing sportswear savvy dudes in denim, donning items of jewellery almost as large as the brands emblazoned on their designer apparel, dwarfing the mobile phones they seemed to have pressed permanently against their ears.

On reaching the corner Daniel turned right, leaving the tight patois and south London slang of the high street behind as he walked along Atlantic Road to the venue on Coldharbour Lane.

The Black Cultural Archive was an Afro-centric bookshop cum exhibition space. Being a bookshop meant it was one of the most neglected and least frequented establishments in Brixton. Most of it books sat gathering dust on its shelves.

Carvings and the yawning faces of the African masks in the window normally looked out on passers-by to little avail, but today was different. Today they looked upon an assembled kindred brought together in an outpouring of community spirit that overflowed its confines onto the street outside.

Daniel could see people standing on the pavement outside as he approached. They were sipping from plastic cups, chatting in the late afternoon sun.

He stepped inside, relieved to find the gathering had a warm buzz about it, one more akin to the atmosphere of a reunion..

Images of Kwame Nkrumah, Marcus Garvey and Patrice Lamumba held pride of place on walls smattered with faded black and white photos of smiling Caribbean's dating from the Windrush era and sixties London.

Assorted flyers and leaflets heralding the reclamation of African heritage, knowledge and pride were available for distant sons and daughters in the hope that they may emulate the absent friend they hoped to see again.

It was a fitting choice of venue, Daniel thought as one of Christian's first goals was to *return* to Africa to understand more about what it meant to be African, not only physically, but more crucially in heart, mind and spirit.

He began his personal journey of discovery by volunteering to work for a charity in Ghana and later he toured West Africa, returning from his travels bearing the name *Njoya Diawara,* a name meaning *Man of Great Spirit*.

Daniel tweaked the brim of his hat and strode though the crowd. He paused to view the images of Christian on his travels in Ghana and in fun-filled moments closer to home that shone from a projector onto a wall.

Christian had always been popular and it seemed his winning looks and personality might also be reflective of the sizable contingent of nubile females in attendance.

One or two inquisitive looks flitted towards the latecomer who had a slight air of foreboding about him, cutting a dash with a degree of panache. Passing on the remnants of a finger buffet, Daniel helped himself to a plastic cup and poured from a bottle of chardonnay and stood sipping, basking in the atmosphere.

It raised his spirit, consigning the stiff mournful reserve of the two-minute silence to where it belonged, a fading realm.

This was a chatty, spirited reunion of friends. It was a union of the faithful, borne of a refusal to lose hope even though Daniel knew Christian's spirit was already among them, albeit on a higher plane.

Daniel bumped into a group of guys he recognised. They were catching up it seemed. Conversation ran along the same familiar preoccupations of property, work, women and associated escapades. So life goes on, Daniel thought, wondering about less earthly matters in light of the purpose for the gathering. This made him begin to think more about the moral values Christian had set himself and how he'd defined success. He too was achievement driven but was preparing himself for greater things by first acquiring self-knowledge.

Daniel tweaked the brim of his hat. His eyes roamed the room for a more interesting conversation to become party to.

He made his way over to a trio of woman, one of whom he'd engaged in a bit of eye tennis with earlier.

He approached with a disarming smile.

'Nana... how've you been?' he said, hanging on her response.

'Er... I don't think so?' came her response.

Her pretty face screwed up into a quizzical frown.

'Sorry. I didn't interrupt your conversation, did I?' he said, offering a polite apology to her friends standing beside her.

'Oh that's it! He exclaimed.

'You were a friend of hers if I remember correctly?'

It was worth a try given that Nana was a customary name across large parts of Ghana.

'So how do you know Christian?' he continued, forging ahead while she searched her memory.

'Uh... from Uni' she replied. One of her friends, the more moodier of the two, inhaled restlessly nudging the other and off they went in search of a more chardonnay.

'Oh Middlesex University' Daniel nodded agreeably.

'Do you know him from athletics' she replied, hazarding a guess based upon her inquisitors stature'

'Ah no. I get asked that a lot though.'

'While I have the sculpted form of a world-class athlete I'm content with just a good workout in the gym.'

'Oh really?' she said, as the beginnings of a smile appeared.

'Yes, just to keep my body in the peak of physical fitness!'

Her face lit up with laughter.

Daniel grinned. He steered the conversation while his mind ran rampant over *her* physical fitness.

Generously proportioned, all the way round, she carried stature as only an African woman could.

Her summer print dress rested snuggly on her curved deep pelvis, the way hips are meant to, hanging down around the thigh drawing the eye down to her strappy-heeled shoes.

Faced with these universal truths and helped by a few cups of chardonnay Daniel's guard slipped momentarily and in this state of flux his judgment faltered.

'I was on the bus you know?' he blurted.

Out it came, sounding as awkward as anything he'd ever said.

Her smile took on a confused look.

Why had he said that? He asked himself, knowing the answer was something in him wanted, *needed* to confide in somebody.

'The same bus Christian was on' he continued, as if elaborating would dig him out of the vast chasm that had just opened up.

He'd wanted to tell somebody for so long, *anyone*, just to get what was troubling him out there.

And what did he expect the response to be? He didn't know, but a force within him yearned for someone to understand.

'The one that was blown up in Tavistock Square?' he offered as the light of interest in her eyes dimmed and her pupils flitted sideways making a mental note of where her friends were.

Too late, too much information, he realised.

Her radiant smile now had an uneasy *get me outta here* edge to it and before Daniel could conjure anything to bridge the stony silence her two friends re-appeared, right on cue answering a sub-womenal mayday alert, to extract their friend from his maniacal clutches.

The 4th Bomb

Aside from the mild embarrassment of her moody friend's mocking stare as she hauled her friend to safety, Daniel realised that he had failed to be understood. This was probably the most basic requirement in the course of human interaction. In his haste to tell what he knew, he'd blown it. It was a lesson. He would have to learn to exercise patience more.

In future he would need to adopt a different strategy, taking a more gradual approach. Things took time for people to understand, especially big terrible *scary* things.

'Dammit!' Daniel exclaimed, suddenly realising the time.

Without consulting his watch he stepped through the crowd, wrestling his phone from his pocket. He was supposed to have met Hilda by now and had to go to the Sainsbury's Express around the corner to buy refreshments for the picnic.

'Hilda, hey where are you? It's Daniel, I'm in Brixton now.'

'Hiya, I'm still indoors, running half an hour late' she replied.

'That's okay, I'll come and meet you. What door number is it?'

'No don't... don't bother' Hilda replied.

'Why not?' Daniel asked.

'Just be where we said. I'll be walking down' She insisted.

'Fair enough, see you shortly' he said, glancing at his watch.

Sainsbury's Express had a nice sparkling Rosé on special offer. That would be a nice treat, Daniel thought.

A pack of four juicy ripened pears, a bottle of mineral water and a large bag of chilli-flavoured nachos joined the bottle in his basket. While queuing up he checked the time again.

It had been 20 minutes since he spoke to Hilda.

After he left Sainsbury's he fine-tuned his hat in the reflection of the shop's darkened window. Turning the corner he passed the a few remaining groups dispersing from the Cultural Archives on his way towards Brixton's old front line, away from the commercial face of Brixton into an older more culturally rooted quarter, evocative of many memories.

Further along Railton Road he passed a small off-licence and the old bakery his father used buy him treats from as a child. He continued on past where they lived in the early seventies. Some way down he stopped and stood on the corner waiting. He looked at the time and sighed. She had declined his offer for him to meet her where she lived, insisting they meet on Railton Road. Now here he was, standing on the street, wearing a panama hat, probably looking like he was waiting to partake in a shady street deal. There was something about Hilda, he thought, this wasn't the first time she'd declined him. The first time was when he first called her to ask her out.

She declined, saying he should notify her 2 weeks in advance! Hardly the spontaneous ways of young people who'd just met. Then again today, not letting him knock on her door.

He stood there tapping his foot impatiently.

He was a singularly driven male who knew precisely what he wanted. Did Hilda know what she wanted? Being a woman could mean that it comprised two completely different and diametrically opposed things, he supposed but it was little things like this that made him think.

'Hello?' He said, trying her number again.

'Hi babes, wait a minute... I can see you! She answered.

Daniel turned round. In the distance he could see her coming towards him with a slightly hurried walk. She was wearing a brown jacket and denims that were tucked into black knee-length boots. An odd combination for such a sunny day, but as she neared his expression couldn't help breaking into a smile, he really was glad to see her.

'Hiya!' she called, her arms reached around him.

He planted his cheek against hers as they hugged briefly.

'Everything okay?' Hilda asked.

'I'm good... so it's still Brockwell Park then?' He asked.

'Yeah, let's hope the sun stays out a bit longer' she replied, as they turned to walk back down the street.

Some way along Hilda pulled out a set of keys from her bag and stopped to open the door of a navy blue Volkswagen Golf. It was an old mark II model, parked tightly between two cars. Its bodywork bore marks from a number of altercations and generally it had the look of a vehicle whose appearance had long ceased being a priority of its owner.

Daniel opened the passenger side door and slid the seat back. After removing items cluttering the foot-well he sat inside and familiarised himself with its unkempt interior while Hilda placed her jacket in the boot. When she took her seat she flashed a quick smile at him as if there was a slim chance that the car wouldn't start. He smiled back at her and after the forth or fifth turn of her key the engine spluttered into life.

Daniel noticed the petrol gauge hovering precariously in the red and how it stayed there while she ricocheted gently between car bumpers to extract the car from its tight spot.

He was about to point this out but resisted the urge, remembering how irate female drivers became if a male dared to suggest how they drive, let alone that they needed to put petrol in the tank. A minute later he *had* to intervene.

'Er, Brockwell Park is that-a-way?' he said sounding ironic, his thumb pointing in the direction behind.

'I know' Hilda said. Daniel eyed his watch discreetly and said nothing more as she drove up Railton Road to Brixton.

From there she turned right before driving around the one way then back up Tulse Hill and left down the far side of Brockwell Park. Then she needed to find a parking space. It would have been far quicker to leave the car where it was and walk 10 minutes to the park by foot, thought Daniel, as her prolonged attempt at parking the car continued.

Aw no! He thought, concealing his frustration. There was more than enough of room. *Acres!*

He was about to tell her to let him park it, but Hilda drove away from the second empty space they came across.

Finally she managed to grab a newly vacated a space on a windy side street just around the corner from Railton road a short while later. They had come full circle. The car was now 10 minutes away from where it had originally been.

Hilda stopped the engine and poked around in her purse.

The car door swung open and her boots set themselves upon the pavement.

'Just popping across the road for some cigarettes' she said.

'Get me a bottle of Lucozade', Daniel called out after her.

As soon she entered the newsagents, a shrill noise sounded. Daniel looked round. The noise was coming from her bag.

It was slightly open so he leaned over and peered inside.

The lit face of her Nokia shone invitingly at him.

Opportunity had presented itself. He wanted to get to know her and a few things made him want to know *more* about her.

Part of him thought she was *too* good to be true, yet another part of him got the impression that at times she was being less than forthright with him. And here was her handbag; the key to finding out all he wanted to know, it's incessant bleat ringing out, almost imploring him to answer it.

The fact that he was even contemplating the thought told him something about how fearful he really was about Hilda or the relationship he assumed they were embarking upon.

Would he be breaking a cardinal sin by answering it or was he just a man battling for peace of mind and assurance, the very thing most people run around every day of their lives in search of? Would this act be healing or damaging, he wondered.

His hand reached in and grasped it. He drew its face closer to his and pressed some buttons to unlock the phone.

It's face lit up, an icon indicated a new text message had arrived. He felt a pang of guilt, thinking that love...the idea of it, or at least a chance of happiness, could hinge on this, as he remembered how Hilda had been a blessing on that day.

If she *was* a blessing, what was he doing?

Love was underpinned by trust. Any happiness they might have was being undermined by his fear.

She had been his angel, yet temptation still beckoned. Daniel hesitated, caught between two minds and two conflicting needs. Curiosity might have got the best of him, had time not intervened. He heard the sound of Hilda's boots clacking against the pavement as she returned to the car. As she swung open the door he slipped the phone back into her bag in the nick of time. She handed him the bottle of Lucozade.

'Pass my bag, babes' She asked. He picked it up and suddenly realised the phones backlight was still illuminated.

He handed her the bag, hoping the phone would automatically lock or he'd have a lot of explaining to do.

'Thanks' she said as she slung it over her shoulder.

Phew, he thought, reaching to the rear seat for the refreshments he bought and they both set off for the park.

As they reached the pedestrian crossing's centre island and waited for the traffic lights to change they both realised.

'Seems they're not letting anymore people in' Hilda said.

'It'll probably be over in ten minutes' sighed Daniel, seeing the line of police outside the main gates barring access.

His suspicions were confirmed when he saw a community police officer turning away a couple with a picnic basket.

The lights changed and he crossed over to the main entrance.

'We've arrived too late' he said, turning to her. But where had she gone, he thought, looking to the left and right of the area in front of the park where people were now streaming out?

Then he noticed Hilda standing behind him, still on the traffic island. He cursed silently. *Meeting him an hour late then taking nearly an hour to find a parking space.* She'd succeeded in ruining this date. He could have spent the afternoon at the gathering for Christian at the archives, he thought, staring at her expression as he stomped back across the road towards her.

She'd probably sabotaged the whole thing, deliberately!

In the end they did manage to spend some quality time albeit of a low quality, in a parking space rather than a park.

It was hardly the relaxed setting Daniel had envisaged, but this is what they did. They spent the next 45 minutes or so sitting in the cramped confines of her car, parked at the side of a road, talking, as pedestrians walked past.

Conversation didn't exactly flow. Maybe it was their surroundings or her car's interior, the subject of which led Hilda to mention how she was going to trade her battle scarred Golf up to a Mazda MX5 convertible; once she'd *sorted out* a place of her own and got herself together that is.

The way the afternoon had gone and her lack of organisation went some way to explaining how maybe she needed to get together, Daniel thought. He listened on, but his mind wandered, concerned with small nagging things.

The sparkling Rosé would have to wait for a more fitting setting, he thought, fuming silently.

~Chapter 9~

The Execution Of Any Man

On Monday the 18th of July the office was abuzz with activity. Noon approached. Daniel scratched an itch on the back of his neck and turned his attention from his work to the Ligali online forum. As he read the pinned topic for an update on the search for Christian he reminded himself that Brendan, his project's manager was back from his holidays and could be lurking on the office's periphery.

http://www.Ligali.org/forum/		
Pinned topic: Ligali Appeal **Member:** Voo **Group:** Moderator	**Posted:**	Jul 8th 2005, 07.30 PM
Greetings Family, *We are seeking help to locate Christian 'Njoya' Small who has been missing since Thursday morning. He was last seen by his flatmate leaving his house on his way to work. Christian works in Holborn and lives in Walthamstow.* *His route would involve changing to the Piccadilly line from the Victoria line either at Finsbury Park or Kings Cross. No one has been able to get in touch with him.* *His work confirmed that he never made it in on Thursday and his mobile constantly goes straight to voicemail.* *If you have any info that may help please contact Toks…*		

He scrolled down through the topic's responses in search of news of Christian but found there had been no news.

When he got back from lunch later that afternoon the news he'd been dreading had come through. It confirmed what he had realised the moment he learnt of Christian's disappearance It was in an email Brian forwarded, on behalf of Tuggstar and Christian's flatmates thanking everyone who attended the gathering on Sunday. Further down the message was confirmation that the police had informed Christian's family he was among the list of fatalities on the night of Friday July 15th.

It went on to explain how the family hadn't announced this on Sunday so as not to cast a shadow on proceedings.

So the police did not inform his family till eight days after the attacks. For eight days there had been shock and disbelief but now the grieving process began, while for Daniel there were questions that needed answering.

TUESDAY 19th JULY

Daniel picked up one of the papers that had been left in the tube carriage. An article in it had the headline *Victims Of Terror*. It featured the faces of those whose lives had been snatched away and blamed followers of a religion it said compelled them to commit murderous acts in the name of God.

The Anglo-Saxon, eastern-European, African, Caribbean and Asian faces each had a picture with a few lines stating their age, occupation and to where they'd been travelling.

'But that's wrong', Daniel thought, staring at the same image of Christian he'd seen on the forum. The newspaper listed him as being a casualty of the Piccadilly tube explosion. Something is not quite right here, he thought. He saw Christian at Euston, *alive* after 9am. That was 15 minutes after the underground blasts had taken place. Christian was heading out of Euston's main concourse towards its bus terminals.

He didn't die on the underground. He died on the bus!

116

This was sloppy journalism of the worst and most insensitive sort, especially after all his family have been through over the last 8 days.

As soon as he reached the office Daniel did an online search for the article. He found the newspaper's website reported the *same* error. On the BBC website a page grouping all 52 victims by the location of the blast that claimed their life had the same mistake. Christian's picture was incorrectly shown among the victims of the Piccadilly line tube blast that took place between Kings Cross and Russell Square. The caption below it claimed his route that day would have involved changing to the Piccadilly Line at Finsbury Park or Kings Cross.

'He was nowhere near the Piccadilly line!' spat Daniel knowing Christian would have intended changing at King's Cross just as he had, but couldn't because it was closed due to three earlier bomb blasts.

On other news websites he found the same error time and time again and he began to realise. Placing Christian on the tube was not a mistake or typographical error. It had been done *intentionally*. Suddenly the 8 day delay in confirming his death and the incidents of men following him began to make sense.

'Damned liars!' Daniel growled under his breath. He knew Christian boarded the Victoria line each morning at Walthamstow where he lived. At that station he could get a seat as the train grew more overcrowded the closer to the city it got. He could've changed at Finsbury Park, but like any commuter naturally opting for quickest and most direct journey to work, he would have remained seated on the Victoria Line all the way to Kings Cross. Like many he'd been unable to get off at Kings cross due to what they were told was a 'power surge' explaining how they had both ended up in Euston that morning. No way Christian could have walked past him after 9am if he died at 8.51am on the Piccadilly tube. 'No way', said Daniel, shaking his head.

He knew what this meant. An uneasy restlessness nestled within him. He needed some space, space to think.

He had to get out of the office. It was only 11.30am, too early to go for lunch. Daniel felt a long spell in the restroom coming on and left the office, walking down three flights of stairs to the male restroom. In a cubicle he sat with his elbows on his knees. Holding his head in his hands he closed his eyes.

In the black stillness the things plaguing his mind were beginning to take on a form, becoming clearer yet seemingly deeper and murkier. After resting for about 10 minutes he leant over the hand basin. Staring at his reflection in the large mirror. He probed the figure that stared back, looking for a sign, a hint or a spark, wondering what kept him beyond the claws of fate and in the arms of destiny.

After a time he conceded *time would be the master* and dried his hands on a paper towel, lobbing it into a bin as he left.

On returning to the office he stopped dead in his tracks then retreated a few steps back into the doorway. His chair had been pushed aside and a burly bald-headed man in a blue boiler suite was lying beneath his desk. No one in the office seemed to mind or even notice the unannounced visitor.

The man had lifted up the carpet and was poking around in his workstation's network router box.

Who was this guy and what was he doing? Daniel wondered.

There was nothing wrong with his PC, and anyway, Patrick from network support was responsible for handling all office hardware or networking issues.

Had the man seen him leave the office and assumed he'd gone to lunch? Daniel asked, hazarding a guess as to why only his workstation's IP box was coming in for scrutiny.

Without confronting the man Daniel turned around and hushed away down the stairs and off to lunch, adding the bald-headed man to the growing list of unexplained incidents of a worrying, but nonetheless curious nature.

WEDNESDAY 20th JULY

To avoid the confusion of their previous meetings Daniel had suggested they meet outside The Globe pub.

It was near Hilda's office on the corner of Moorgate and London Wall, so they managed to meet at the appointed time.

Daniel's black shirt had a feint pattern embroidered through it. He wore it open-necked with a pair of charcoal grey slacks.

On his feet were a pair of tan brogues like the ones he'd worn on July the 7th.

He'd bought a new pair; exact same design and colour.

In the window of the menswear shop next to the pub he could see the reflections of people crossing the road.

He discarded the piece of gum he was chewing when he saw Hilda appear wearing a plain white blouse and a black skirt.

Today she had done her hair differently. It was tied back; a look which made her facial features more prominent.

'Hi babes' she sang.

'Hey, look at your hair… I like it' he said.

'Aw, I was in a rush this morning' she explained, sweeping a lock of hair out of her eye with her hand.

'A friend's plaiting it for me this weekend'

'Nothing special, just a bit more manageable' she added.

'Cool' Daniel said, holding open the pub door for her.

They creaked up a narrow staircase to a dining room that had high ceilings and a sedate air.

Inside the unhurried clink and genteel scrape of cutlery against china could be heard.

Daniel chose a table with a nice vantage point, one where sunlight streamed in through a window and he could see out across to the London Metropolitan University buildings and the top of a grey spire hidden from the busy street below.

Daniel Obachike

The sturdy wooden table they sat at looked weathered rather than antiquated, but Daniel was content being anywhere the sun shone, with a nice view and nice company.

'So what are you having?' he asked Hilda, as he steadily eyed a man seated on the other side of the room.

The man rustled his broadsheet. Hilda scrutinised the menu. She had a look of uncertainty on her face. The man was of smart appearance and looked in his late twenties.

He had sensibly styled neat blonde hair and wore his shirt open-necked. The shirt had a red and white check with bits of blue piping through it. It was no casual shirt; it was a double-cuffed Windsor collar, adding to the upper-class air he gave off as he peered over the newspaper, paying more attention to Daniel than any article in his paper.

Daniel turned away pondering over the dreamy spire outside as he reached for his Nokia.

When he met the man's gaze a second time, the man reacted by folding his paper and placing it on the table before hurriedly making his way out of the dining room.

Hilda was still staring emptily into the menu when the waitress came over to their table.

'Are you ready to order?' the waitress asked.

'A pint of Stella Artois and one mineral water', said Daniel.

'Bottled please' Hilda emphasised.

'And… I'll go for the spicy beef sausages with cheesy mashed potato' he said, pausing as the waitress took his order.

'And can you make sure there's enough gravy?' he asked.

Hilda folded her menu placing it on the table.

'The same please'

'*Without* gravy' she stressed.

The drinks arrived and the food followed some time after. Daniel unfurled the cutlery from its paper napkin and immediately got stuck in.

'Mmmm, the cheesy mash is nice' he pointed out to Hilda who sat prodding a spicy sausage around on her plate.

'Is everything okay?' he asked, noticing Hilda didn't seem her usual chirpy self.

'Uh, I don't know' she said, placing her knife and fork down on the white linen tablecloth.

'My belly feels a bit weird'

'Huh? You've barely touched the plate' Daniel said, tucking in. Hilda put it more succinctly for him.

'I've lost my appetite' she said, scrunching up her nostrils as though the food turned her stomach.

Holding a napkin to her mouth she pushed the plate away.

'Okay' Daniel accepted, wary of her insistent look, not wishing to daub another patch of grey to the chinks of cloud appearing in the face of his sunshiny horizon.

'I'll have it then' he offered, harpooning one of the bangers on her plate with his fork.

Between mouthfuls he looked up at her face to gauge her response. She was rummaging around in her bag.

'Mind if I smoke?' she asked, pulling out a box of cigarettes.

'I think it's no smoking actually', he answered.

She frowned and plonked the packet of cigarettes on the table.

Why was she was being moody? Daniel wondered, smearing a piece of sausage in the pool of gravy on his plate. What had he done? Or not done? Had he messed up somewhere?

'Is your stomach feeling any better?' he asked, after some time.

'A bit' she replied, sounding as if she needed a second opinion.

'So… if you're getting your hair done this weekend when will you be coming to mine?' Daniel asked, pressing the question despite her mood.

'I dunno… I'll let you know' she replied, glancing at her watch. As soon as the waitress came over with the bill Hilda began gathering up her bag in readiness to leave.

Daniel downed the remainder of his pint, left some notes on the saucer and exchanged an understanding smile with the waitress as he followed Hilda out the door.

'I'll walk you back to your office' he said, once they were outside.

'No, it's okay I'm fine' Hilda said, sounding like she wanted to be left alone.

Not wishing to part with any ill-feeling or misunderstanding between them Daniel continued walking next to her doggedly.

'Look!' Hilda said, turning to him.

For a split second she looked him steadily in the eye, then she seemed to retreat, adopting a lower tone.

'Just give me a call Friday about the weekend, yeah?'

Daniel was about to ask her something, but held back.

He stood outside the Globe pub for a while, watching her as she walked back towards her office in Moorgate.

He kept watching her until pedestrians obscured her from his vision in the distance.

THURSDAY 21st JULY

It had been two weeks to the day since he scrambled from the wrecked bus. Two weeks since his waking hours became stranger than his wildest dreams. This morning he found himself watching the clocks slow creep towards 09.47.

As the time drew near he braced himself for an imaginary impact. Around him his colleagues, immersed in their work didn't mark the moments passing, but Daniel observed it sipping thoughtfully from a cup of lukewarm tea, before setting about the workload that needed a good trimming back.

Later on he wondered how Hilda was.

He hoped she was feeling better than when they last met as his eye re-read the short email he was about to send her.

Maybe he just needed to make more of an effort, he thought, as he pressed the send button. That's it. He would go down to her office one day and surprise her. Flowers…or something like that, as a kind of thank you, women love being fussed over.

By the time lunchtime approached he'd made reasonable headway and was poised to begin roaming the Internet when something told him not to. It was a strange sensation, one that made him feel like he was being observed.

Slowly he spun his chair around with a broad disarming smile at the ready, fully expecting to meet the disapproving stare of Brendan Meade over his shoulder, but it wasn't the slightly built bespectacled project manager standing there.

Behind him stood a man, the *same* man he'd seen the previous day in the dining room above the pub. He even wore the same checked shirt he wore the previous day.

The man stared intently at him. Daniel smirked, glanced round at his colleagues who were still engrossed in their work then back at the man, offering him a shrug of the shoulders and a glib smile before returning to his screen.

What are you playing at? Daniel wondered. His mind raced.

His hands hovered over his PC's keyboard as though he'd forgotten what the symbols on the keys signified.

His brain was caught in momentary stasis trying to comprehend what was happening. Forces were moving around him. Intelligence officers busied themselves; intelligence operatives scurried to and fro. For what purpose?

Why was *he* of interest to them? They'd already named 4 suspects. Daniel glanced back at the man again. His public schoolboy air of superiority had turned to a look of distain.

Clearly he hadn't taken too kindly to being *made* twice in 48 hours. Daniel leant forward reaching for the Nokia on his desk, but before he could change it to capture mode, the man quickly made himself scarce, passing silently out of office while none but Daniel was any the wiser to his intrusion.

At 12.30pm he had nearly finished rattling off responses to the many emails in his inbox when all of a sudden there was a power cut. Dammit, he thought.

Hoots of delight accompanied the odd groan that resounded in unison as the *second* power-cut in two days happened without warning. They had ten minutes to back up their work before the emergency generator cut-out and consigned any unsaved data to another dimension.

James stood up and looked out of the window at surrounding buildings. He could make out the illuminated neon signage in the windows of bars near the Intelsat building on the other side of Old Street.

'Look's like its localised to this side of Old Street' he said.

'How long before the powers back?' moaned Dave.

'A couple of hours, maybe' answered Tariq, hazarding a guess.

Being more or less lunchtime, Dan convened a small group of the I.T guys and used the opportunity to have an extended team lunch. By 13.15pm most of them had drifted down to the JD Weatherspoon's pub around the corner.

Twenty minutes later Daniel joined them. He entered the pub passing a few scary looking career drinkers sitting at the front on his way to the bar. There he ordered a pint, before joining his colleagues at the pub's rear where Guinness and ale were already flowing as they waited for food to arrive.

'Steak-kidney pie and chips?' Asked the barman, balancing a plate in one hand before placing it in front of one of their number.

'Cheesecake?'

'*Cheesecake*?' gasped an astonished James.

'Who ordered cheesecake!' he asked indignantly.

'Oui!' called Oliviere diminutively.

Hysterical laughter rang out as their colleague provided yet more fodder for their barrage of banter.

A volley of gleeful shots followed and Oliviere's role as the butt of humorous digs would surely have continued had the words *Breaking News* not flashed across the bottom of the pubs plasma screen TV.

'Oh look, ere we go again!' said Ainsworth, directing their attention to the screen as he supped his ale.

Initial reports… 4 bomb explosions go off around London.

'Gosh, two weeks on and it happens again!' spouted James.

At first there was a hushed silence, as news reports of 4 more bombs came in, but the amount of alcohol already consumed meant the Sky News coverage was met with a certain amount of glee. A succession of terror-related quips ensured Daniel became the butt of the hilarity.

He absorbed the humorous digs and the news sipping steadily from his glass and for once Oliviere was not the target.

The lack of casualties reported only increased their bombast. Whereas two weeks before people had rung friends and family praying they were safe and well, today they rang-up their mates like it was the latest funny gag.

A short time later, Daniel's mobile let out a sharp tone and he scooped it up off the table in front of him.

'Hey Brian, my man whats-up?' He said.

'Have you heard, there've been more bombings, are you okay, where are you?' Brian asked, in a worried tone.

'I'm sitting in a pub, having a drink!' Daniel replied.

'It wasn't me mate… *honest bruv*' he laughed, taking the reports in a similar vein as the rest of his colleagues.

'They say the bombers used Fitness First bags but the bombs failed to detonate' said Brian, sounding concerned.

'Did they?' replied Daniel, sounding intrigued.

'Maybe the bombers decided on a speedier weight loss regime?' he replied chuckling.

FRIDAY 22nd JULY

The next day a hushed silence fell around the office. Staff had gathered around the small monitor. Reports were coming through that one of the attempted bombers from the previous day had been apprehended.

James swiveled round in his chair wielding the remote, increasing the volume. Daniel walked over, straining to hear the newscaster.

Those huddled round the screen saw footage taken from a helicopter flying over Stockwell, South London.

Ambulances, police cars and armed response vehicles could be seen. Policemen sealing off the area waved members of the public away in scenes, which were all too familiar.

Suspect apprehended. I repeat, a suspect wanted in connection with yesterdays failed terror attacks has been apprehended in Stockwell underground station in South London.

The news anchor handed over to a live broadcast at the scene.

'Early indications are that the suspect was challenged by armed police who opened fire' said the reporter.

Eyebrows were raised around the office.

'At this time details of the suspect's condition are sketchy'

'Betcha he's innocent' muttered Daniel.

'Ha! That'd be a result' scoffed James as Daniel returned to his desk pondering this development.

More than anyone, he knew that it could've been *any man* who the gunmen shot in this climate of fear and confusion and two weeks ago *any man* could have been him.

He sat at his desk and recalled the pang of uncertainty he felt just before he scrambled to his feet and fled the shattered bus.

Luckily for him the only thing they had been shooting immediately after the blast in Tavistock Square had been video footage.

127

That evening after work on his way to meet Hilda he had more personal concerns on his mind recalling the strained atmosphere the last time they met.

He saw her standing across the road from Moorgate tube.

The station's entrance was manned either side by Evening Standard vendors who's news-stands headline triumphantly proclaimed '*WE GOT HIM*!'

Hilda pulled her bag tighter to her shoulder when she spotted Daniel approaching.

'So where are we going?' she asked, as they stepped briskly amongst commuters scurrying off for their weekend.

'A film… let's go and watch something in Leicester Square!' he suggested, having somewhere dark and intimate in mind.

'Aren't you hungry?' Hilda asked.

'I feel like having some sushi… I know just the place'.

Daniel didn't argue, recalling how their last meal had gone as they headed into the underground station.

A couple of hours later they emerged from a Yo Sushi! bar in Soho trailing through side streets towards Leicester Square.

Daniel glimpsed at the receipt again before rubbing his eyes and stuffing it in his back pocket. His credit card was nearly £70.00 heavier. Hilda had ordered a second mini-bottle of Veuve Cliqout champagne at £14.00 a pop before choosing to tell him her company messed up her wages and could *he* get it! As he'd drawn out his plastic he could have sworn he'd heard that line somewhere before and he wondered, wages *messed-up* by the company she'd been working for four years for?

They passed a pub with drinkers standing on the pavement outside enjoying the warm weather then by a row of trendy looking shops.

'Wait a minute' Daniel said, disappearing into a small Chinese shop next door, leaving Hilda gazing into the window of a boutique displaying handbags.

Inside the shop an elderly Chinese gentleman sitting in the corner cackled at him. Daniel turned around browsing the assorted foodstuffs and dried ingredients in large jars while waiting for the attendant to acknowledge his presence.

She was in no rush.

After heaping three tablespoons of dried herbs of some sort into a large stainless steel kettle she turned to him.

'What can I get you?' she asked rapidly.

Daniel replied saying the first thing that popped into his head.

'Er, a green tea please… to take away.'

'Make that a small', he added, noting the large polystyrene cup her hand veered towards while keeping an eye on the street outside through the window.

A minute later and £1.35 pence lighter he stood outside the shop. Where had she gone? He wondered, looking up and down the street. Two minutes later Hilda stepped out of the boutique next door with a smile on her face, but by the time she reached him her expression had changed.

'Why didn't you get me one?' she asked.

'You didn't ask for one' Daniel answered flatly, recalling how she'd cajoled him into buying two mini-bottles of champagne not less than an hour before. He knew she grudgingly realised this as they walked through the backstreets of Soho towards the tourist packed part of Leicester Square in silence.

Given this he might have guessed what was coming next.

By the time they reached the cinema in Leicester Square Hilda had changed her mind. She didn't want to see a film anymore.

Daniel stopped and turned to her.

'Hilda' he said, quite directly.

'Why is it every time we meet, you always seem to change plans at the last moment for some reason?'

'Can't you just do something for the sheer sake of it?' he asked, staring at her.

Hilda had a slightly confused look, confused at being pursued and challenged at the same time. She didn't seem to have a response to his question so he tried to help her out.

'Well what *do* you feel like doing?' he asked in a smoother tone knowing gruffness would not ease the situation.

Hildas's eyes narrowed and a familiar wry smile returned to her face.

'Let's get some ice cream?' she replied.

'Hmm… okay' Daniel said, after a moments consideration. Seeing that they were right next to a Haagen Daas café, he would let her slide, *this time*.

After a while they sat with two scoops of macadamia nut and vanilla ice cream each on a bench in Leicester Square, watching tourists pass by. They tried to agree what they would do together on the weekend.

Daniel didn't need too much imagination of what he wanted to do, but his head told him there was still much he had to know about Hilda.

~Chapter 10~

Counselling With Julia Brown

A week later Daniel left work early for an appointment at 4pm. Why his session had been moved from the Cannon Hill clinic to his G.P's surgery at the last minute he didn't know.

He arrived at the G.P surgery at Abernathy House a few minutes late and confirmed his arrival for the appointment at the reception desk.

He knocked on a door and when a voice called out he entered.

The counsellor had been waiting for him.

She wore a green cardigan, trousers and white socks and sat across from an empty chair that Daniel settled in.

He studied her face. Her smile looked warm and kind.

A profusion of white streaked across her short grey hair.

Her skin indicated her senior years. It had hundreds of tiny wrinkles so fine it seemed like delicate crepe paper that would tear at the slightest touch.

His hand felt inside his shirt's front pocket and pressed the record button as Julia Brown introduced herself.

She began by asking him about what happened after the explosion and how he felt he was coping.

'Er well… I got home okay that day I suppose' he began.

'And went back to work the following day really. There seemed nothing else to do'

'Then… after… that weekend… things started changing.'

'Changing?' she echoed, in a tone suggesting change was a rare and unusual phenomenon.

'A few guys… I began to notice them… trailing me.'

'On public transport?' she asked.

'Everywhere… in my apartment block, on my way to and from work, in the park, around my local area…'

'And how do you feel about travelling on public transport now, Daniel?' she asked after a pause. He inhaled deeply.

'Er, sometimes on public transport I feel a bit paranoid every now and then, I guess. More so, than the average commuter' he replied. The counsellor nodded sympathetically.

'Why do you believe there are people following you?'

'Well…' he said; sensing things were about to get complicated.

'Because of what I witnessed on the bus in Tavistock Square'

'They've followed me… they gained access to my apartment on at least two occasions'

'Really?' she said, hastily scribbling down notes.

'Can you describe how you realised this' she asked.

'Yeah. I came home the first time. I was about to dismiss it as nothing, but then I noticed in an ashtray by the TV in the lounge where I leave 20 pence pieces that come in handy for the parking meters. Someone had replaced the five silver coins I'd left with a single pound coin'

'It's like they're trying to play mind games with me, sending a signal, a signal saying they can do whatever they like.'

Daniel sighed, noting the slight intake of breath as Julia Brown paused. He realised, there wasn't much he could do to stop it and there was nothing stopping Julia Brown from drawing whatever conclusions she had from his replies.

'And… who are *they*?' she asked after a pregnant pause.

'Er… British intelligence I guess, MI5 or something'

'I couldn't tell precisely as they didn't leave a calling card… I suppose that's why they're called the secret service.'

Sitting there revealing this to her, made Daniel determined to do something about it. She just sat there nodding and smiling.

Right there and then Daniel resolved to be prepared for them the next time. Not so much *preventing* entry but *proving* entry.

The counsellor turned over a leaf on her pad and began asking him about his family background and education.

'My background, I'm Nigerian... born in London, studied to a Masters Degree level, er... what else do you want to know?' He asked with a shrug of his shoulders.

Soon her desk clock indicated the 50 minute mark had arrived.

She wrapped up giving him a parting smile, but instead of feeling a weight lifted from his shoulders as he imagined, Daniel left the session feeling frustrated.

The forces wrestling within him still sought understanding.

He failed to see how chatting to some nice old lady had helped. Maybe the cosy counselling session helped Julia Brown?

She didn't understand him so she sat there observing him like an item of curiosity, attempting to classify him, failing to even grasp what had *happened* to him. The session didn't seem to have had much point. He may as well have not bothered, he thought as he left the G.P's surgery.

If it were not for his sister's insistence he probably would not have returned. It was she who managed to convince him to continue attending the remaining sessions.

'Well okay then!' Daniel grudgingly accepted.

Initially he'd asked his doctor for someone with experience of counselling bomb survivors, mentioning a few clinics in London he'd got off the web whose staff had experience helping survivors from bomb attacks in Northern Ireland, but Dr Gocman wanted him to have sessions with some old biddy. And what did he get? A relationship counsellor, a cup of tea and a shoulder to cry on.

Julia Brown probably fully understood the mind-state of post-menopausal women, but clearly found herself wanting when it came to understanding an African male and the emotions emanating from what he was going through.

It was symptomatic of the lack of assistance he'd heard many other survivors from the bombings had experienced.

By the fifth session Daniel suspected Julia Brown felt she was not benefiting from their meetings as much as he was.

Her frustration began to tell. It may have been that he was getting used to their cosy little chats when he replied to one of her increasingly aimless questions in too philosophical a manner. All the same, Daniel was quite surprised.

It was as though he'd flicked a switch. Her face turned red.

'There's nothing wrong with you!' she spouted sternly.

'Erm, you may have a point' Daniel said, reclining in the chair.

'But that's not really the point is it?' he countered.

She seethed silently and continued angrily scribbling down something on her pad.

'When does understanding what I'm going through end?'

'When I'm healed?' he asked.

'Maybe its when justice is served' he said.

Counselling had proved to be beneficial, he'd been told he should keep them up and he was beginning to see the benefits and now she now accusing him of wasting her time?

Later on Daniel smirked as he played back the recording of their final session and considered the fact:

If a western lady of pension-able age *had* understood a young African man emotionally then he would have *really* known he had a problem, *a big problem*.

~Chapter 11~

Night Moves

Seven Sisters was ideally located on the Victoria line, situated midway between his apartment in North London and South London where Hilda was.

All was quiet as Daniel stood outside Seven Sisters underground station that evening but he had good reason to remain alert. It was due to his brushes with the intelligence operatives but also in part to the slight air of uncertainty he'd almost come to expect with Hilda.

Her phone kept diverting to voicemail. It probably meant she was still journeying underground, he imagined, hoping there would be no last minute change of plan.

A gust of evening breeze encouraged him to go down into the station to wait there for her. Nothing would go wrong, he assured himself. She would just arrive a bit late and a bit unorganised, as she always seemed to.

His tenseness dissipated when she appeared 15 minutes later at the top of the escalator with her bag over one elbow and a large weekend bag in the other hand.

'Hiya!' she waved, as she reached the ticket barrier.

The navy blue Mac she wore had a belt tied at her waist that extenuated her figure. It was at odds with the denim jeans she had on. They did little for the svelte figure they concealed.

She was being cautious, he thought, taking the precaution of wearing jeans on the first night at his place.

'You okay?' he asked, pecking her lightly on both cheeks.

'Fine… you been waiting long?' Hilda asked.

'Nah, not long' he replied, practicing the patience she'd tested.

'Let me…' he offered, hoisting her large bag over his shoulder.

'Jeez, what've you got in here?' he asked, as they walked away.

'You're staying overnight, not moving in!'

'Just my outfit' she replied with a smile.

'Oh… I see' he said, casting her a knowing glance.

'A nun's outfit? Or a leopard skin cat-suit perhaps?'

'Ha, you wish!' laughed Hilda.

'Just my clothes for tomorrow' she giggled, noting his face looked ready to burst into a broad smile.

Outside they strode past the late-night grocers and off-licenses to Seven Sisters train station to catch a train back to Enfield.

Back at his block they walked up the steps to the entrance.

Kieran looked up from his desk as they entered and crossed the lobby. Daniel ignored him but sensed him ogling his companion as they waited for the lift to arrive. Once they got upstairs he opened door to his apartment and Hilda entered.

The space she stepped into was a spartan one. With white walls and hardwood flooring, black marble worktops and brushed steel appliances, everything either had its place or was tucked out of sight. He lived in a world of his own design and this was it, lifestyle masquerading as life, perhaps, but Daniel could see Hilda was impressed. He noticed her look of surprise as he dimmed the lights in the lounge, instantly changing the room's ambience. A warm hum kicked in as he flicked on the heating. Hilda wandered into the room removing her coat and with a small pirouette she turned, handing it to him.

'Nice place!' she said, familiarising herself with its interior as she made herself comfortable on an angular pale green sofa.

Daniel sat down next to her and with a remote turned on the television. The hot talking point was the Stockwell shooting.

Reports were now suggesting that the Brazilian man wore a denim jacket and may have ran from his gun-toting pursuers because he'd over-stayed his visa. This was a departure from the opinions of an unnamed bystander who told reporters at the scene that the victim was wearing a big black padded coat that had wires dangling out.

What was apparent was the British media's discomfort on learning that such a horrendous act could be carried out at the behest of a state *supposedly* as democratic as the U.K.

More excuses and possible explanations appeared trying to justify the innocent man's execution.

The frozen stare of a man named Jean Charles de Menezes held a particular resonance. Daniel, remembered a second before he leapt from the bombed bus, a dark variable flashed through his mind issuing a similar caption. *Shot Man, Mistaken For Bomber*.

Although Chief of Police, Sir Ian Blair was unavailable for comment, an Independent Police Complaints enquiry was announced which would report its findings at a later date.

'Ah yes, an IPCC enquiry. The Brazilian's family must be breathing a huge sigh of relief' muttered Daniel, with a large dollop of sarcasm. He looked at Hilda. Her look of disinterest told him she wasn't concerned either way. She *must* have at heard about it, he thought or was he presuming too much.

He supposed there were some who didn't know or care one iota about matters affecting the society in which they lived. Then again, maybe rants were not the best way to start the evening, he thought, seeing Hilda's blank expression.

He was supposed to be entertaining, showing her a good time. That was what she wanted, not his opinions on world affairs.

'Oh well' he harped jollily, trying to restore a lighter tone.

He zapped the news channel and went to check what was in the fridge. As he emptied some snacks into a bowl he couldn't help thinking. He hadn't looked for some kind of approval from Hilda but had expected a flicker of emotion at least.

After all, she had been in Tavistock Square that day just as he had. Surely July the 7th meant something to her?

'Did you rent any films?' came her response.

'Er… I've got a couple we could watch' he said hopefully.

'Have a look… on top of the DVD player' he said, taking two glasses out from the open-plan kitchen's cabinets.

'Okay' she said, in a far away tone. Her attention was divided as she was reading a text that had just arrived on her phone.

'Can I get you a drink?' Daniel offered.

'Pardon?' she replied, busily typing a response.

'I said would you like a *drink*?'

'Er, no… no thanks' she said, taking a quick glance up him.

'I see you brought some refreshment of your own?' he said noticing the bottle of water poking out of her bag on the floor beside her.

'I'll just have to drink this *alcohol-laced* wine myself, then you can take advantage of me instead!' he said grinning, still trying to bring a lighter tone to proceedings.

Half a bottle of wine later the sound of R'n'B playing in the background contrasted with the acrimonious bickering on the Big Brother reality show they were watching.

It was one of the rare occasions Daniel was glad *Big Brother* was on as it was the type of program *everyone* had an opinion of some sort on.

'I think Makosi will get evicted', Hilda said.

'How do you mean? Maxwell will!' argued Daniel.

'She's won it, hands down! She's playing 'em like an old accordion' he laughed gleefully. After a few glasses of wine the onscreen hilarity and company had raised his spirits.

Hilda seemed all the more beguiling. He'd been watching her closely, searching for a hint or cue as to her true feelings.

For some time he had sensed that Hilda seemed preoccupied with something, becoming increasingly guarded the closer he got to her.

The 4th Bomb

So far the evening felt like it had on the Victoria line tube on the morning on 7/7, when he sat next to the sister on the tube.

He'd wanted to say something on that occasion, but similarly external factors had intruded. Something, he didn't know quite what, had got in the way.

He looked at Hilda. They hadn't tugged each other's clothes off 10 minutes after arriving at his apartment, which may or may not indicate that it wasn't primarily a physical attraction. Sometimes love needs time. Maybe that's what is was it, or maybe she wanted something else?

Until he knew precisely what it was, he would continue to proceed cautiously, especially with that time approaching.

He had her. Cornered. At last, but he felt strangely cornered himself only this he had to override his intuition and dispense with etiquette, *manners* or logic because time and opportunity had crossed paths. He gently seized the moment bringing his hand up to her cheek in a caress, pulling her head towards his.

Their lips touched briefly. He looked at her then he kissed her again. He'd been sitting beside her, waiting and wishing they could communicate as freely as they had on that terrible day, but now only one language made any sense.

His left arm had slipped around her waist in preparedness for a further manoeuvre when suddenly a loud tone stabbed the carefully cultivated ambience.

Hilda turned away and plucked her phone from its perch on the arm of the sofa.

'Gotta take this' she whispered and before it could ring again she'd sprung up out of the door to answer it in the hallway.

Daniel remained seated as the door slowly swung shut behind her. He popped a handful of popcorn into his mouth, chewing it thoughtfully while the squabbles onscreen continued and he waited for Hilda's conversation to end. Ten minutes later she returned and sat down on the couch beside him with a sigh.

'Sorry 'bout that' she said on her return.

'It was my mum. Y'know how mum's can get sometimes... they just go *on and on*' she explained.

'Yeah, tell me about it' Daniel replied, nodding in agreement.

The last track on the CD ended and he got up and pressed the eject button. In the bedroom next door he returned the disc to is case in one of the stacks of CD's neatly piled against the wall according to genre.

Before returning to the lounge he paused in the hall observing his guest through the door's glass panel. He saw her yawn and stretch her body from the corner of the sofa she'd confined herself to. Then she puffed up some cushions before re-settling into a more relaxed posture.

Daniel returned to the bedroom and made a final check.

His hand puffed up the pillows and smoothed a crease out of the duvet on his bed. In the corner a floor standing lampshade was turned down as low as the filament would allow then a final scan of the room's general tidiness was made.

He checked his reflection in the fitted wardrobes full-length mirror. Was everything was set? It seemed so, he thought, and he returned to the lounge.

'We may as well call it a night' he said, simulating a yawn 20 minutes later. Hilda agreed and they retired to the bedroom.

When it was her turn to prepare and change into her nightclothes she entered the en-suite bathroom with her night bag. A few minutes later she emerged wearing a peach colored silk dressing gown with her hair tied up in a headscarf.

She was greeted by the sight of Daniel lying on his side on the duvet wearing nothing but boxer shorts and a cheeky smirk.

'What side do you prefer?' he said, patting the mattress firmly.

'This side will do', She said primly. Her nightgown fell from her shoulders just before she slipped under the duvet.

Even though Daniel didn't feel the need to rush things, it was always a good idea to test the water, he thought and now that Hilda was here, he felt things could do with a little *prod*.

140

Lifting up the duvet he took a good look at her nightdress.
'Very nice' he purred. Hilda glanced over her shoulder at him, with a look of slight surprise as his gaze swept along her body. He grabbed her by the waist, pulling her body towards his. Pressed up against her, he felt her body's warmth.
Daniel smiled at her and placed a goodnight kiss on her cheek before releasing her.
Hilda rolled back onto her side facing away. Daniel turned and slid the dimmer switch to darkness leaving nothing but the illuminated digits of the radio alarm clock aglow.
'Night-night, he said.
'Goodnight' came her reply and Daniel's open eyes wandered in the silence as he waited for tiredness to envelop him.

The next morning he stepped out of the shower and rubbed himself down with a towel. After applying moisturiser to his skin he smeared a hole in the condensation on the mirror and began brushing his teeth.

'Train leaves in half an hour, start getting a move on!' he called out through a mouthful of foamed toothpaste.

Hadn't she heard him? He came out of the bathroom and took a pair of navy blue trousers and a white shirt off a wooden hanger in the wardrobe. As he pulled on the trousers he saw Hilda stirring in the wardrobe mirrors reflection.

'Did you hear me!' he repeated, chuckling on seeing her sleepy eyed-face. She woke and reached for her dressing gown.

Daniel took a fresh towel out of a drawer.

'There you go… don't say I never give you nothing' he said, tossing it onto the duvet as she tightened her nightgown's belt around her waist. She took a few ungainly steps across the hardwood floor to the en-suite and closed the door behind her.

The hiss of the power-shower starting-up was heard as Daniel fastened his shirt buttons. While pulling his socks on he sat on the bed and noticed her phone lying beside the pillow.

'Hmmm' he thought. She'd slept with it under the pillow.

He picked it up, unlocked it and scrolled through her recent call list. The last caller's ID was hidden so he browsed her recent text messages finding one that had been received the previous evening.

'Hmmm' he muttered thoughtfully, reading the message.

He pressed the *more* button to reveal the sender's number and opened the bedside cabinet to retrieve a pen to note it down.

Paper. He needed something to write on. Duh! Just his luck, there wasn't a scrap on hand anywhere in the room he'd ensured was meticulously clean the night before.

The sound of the shower running could still be heard when a click, alerted him to the bathroom door unlocking.

Its chrome handle turned, the door opened and Hilda stood in a shower cap glaring at him with a contemptuous gaze.

'Is the water temperature okay?' asked Daniel staring back. 'These Italian designer bathroom fittings can be a tad temperamental at times.'

Hilda stomped out with a hand clasped across her, keeping the towel firmly wrapped around her.

She scooped her phone up from where Daniel had hurriedly dropped it beside the pillow. She looked at it then glared back at him knowing full well that he'd gone though her handset, *invading* her privacy.

Daniel stared back at her, half-defiant, half so-what? He wasn't going to admit it and she knew it, even though the phones backlight was still lit when she'd picked it up.

Privacy? What about it? Privacy has no place in *his* bed. Especially not if what he suspected might be going on, *was* going on. To avoid a scene in his bedroom, Daniel stopped himself from asking the obvious or doing anything too hasty.

Hilda said nothing and stomped indignantly back into the bathroom as Daniel's face contorted into a wry grin.

He put on his shoes and went into the kitchen area to forage around for breakfast.

By the time he'd finished Hilda was still getting dressed.

He stood in the hall tapping his feet impatiently, waiting for her in readiness to depart for Enfield Town train station.

Given the hushed silence as they both left his block it wasn't hard to tell there was something on Hilda's mind.

Daniel could understand perfectly well why there wasn't the joy of lovers strolling hand in hand in the heady afterglow of love, making plans for the future that morning.

Still he thought it spoke volumes how Hilda made no mention of his earlier misdemeanor. Was her guilt greater than his?

In return he didn't ask her whom the text message was from.

The journey to work would have been even more strained had it not been for the enforced silence of the grey brigade aboard the train. Hilda got a seat while Daniel stood all the way to Liverpool Street Station.

A few times he saw her look at her watch with a dour expression on her face. She couldn't blame him for that one, he thought. She had been the one delaying them this morning.

As the 08:27 from Enfield Town reached its destination, commuters stood up ready to burst from its carriages.

Among them Daniel and Hilda crossed Liverpool Street's concourse following the stream of city workers.

Once they reached City Road Daniel continued walking with Hilda in the direction of her office.

'Aren't you going to work?' Hilda said, breaking the silence.

'Yeah… in a bit.' he replied.

'Why's that then?' she asked in an enquiring tone.

'Cos I have to use the Abbey National cash machine. It's just past your office in Moorgate'

'Oh' said Hilda nodding slowly.

As they neared the cash point Hilda turned to him.

'Can you lend me some money? I'll pay you back. I'm a bit short, work messed up my salary and I want to get a sandwich'

'Huh, okay' he said, as he entered his pin number.

First she's late, now she wants to stop for a sandwich.

'There you go' he said, handing her a £20 pound note.

'Thanks', she replied, folding the money as they headed back.

'Okay then, I'll see you later on' she said, as she joined the queue in a small sandwich deli a short distance from her office in Moorgate.

'You'll call me yeah?' she asked.

'Er… I'll email you. I've a lot on this week' he said, and he headed off in the direction of Old Street wondering about the direction their dates were leading.

~Chapter 12~

Fallen Angel

A man with a flustered expression brushed hurriedly past as Daniel walked ponderously along City Road.

Hilda still filled his thoughts as he approached the building at Old Street, but now the thoughts were no longer gentle ones. They were serious doubts.

He had to question everything she'd said about herself.

Thinking back, he'd erred heavily on the side of caution since encountering the trio on his early morning jog days after 7/7. Everything going on around him stemmed from what happened in Tavistock Square, from what he'd seen, and he met Hilda that morning minutes after the explosion.

Had she been there completely by chance? He asked, recalling the moment he first laid eyes on her outside Lynton House where shocked survivors were being taken to get assistance.

Her brown eyes pierced through the mayhem in his direction. She was on her way to work, she'd said and they both came through the terror, through the storm *together*.

But if he searched his true feelings now, he would have to confess he didn't know her any better than he did on July 7th. Six weeks on, the distance between them felt like that of strangers. The tension surrounding their subsequent meetings had made it increasingly apparent. That was why he'd kept his emotions on a leash, waiting for some kind of sign, but she hadn't given him any. Whatever she was concealing about herself, she was in no hurry to be more forthcoming.

She'd just been leading him on, from the start.

For what purpose? He wondered.

All that week Daniel's lunchtimes followed a similar pattern.

He sat on a bench with his sandwich, watching people on their lunch-break and couples who'd managed to escape the office, grabbing a few moments together in Finsbury Circus.

Daniel retraced his own steps with Hilda. He recalled how he'd walked on clouds as they left Tavistock Square together, how the grey masonry of the buildings they passed and the granite of the pavement they stepped on had sparkled. Each and every mesmerising flower he saw had a shimmering aura.

It was amazing. How could he have glimpsed things so wonderful moments after witnessing something so atrocious?

And then they went to Witan Jardine, Hilda's agency at Southampton row in Holborn.

He accompanied her partially because all public transport in central London was suspended, but mainly because he didn't want to be apart from her.

There they had stayed, talking till late that afternoon, when they began the long walk from the city to south London.

Now he knew what he hadn't realised then.

They weren't meant for each other, even though their meeting had been heaven sent.

Daniel finished his sandwich and sipped from a carton of juice. The desire to understand what it all meant was growing.

He already held some pieces of the puzzle; the missing gaps in reality he saw in Tavistock Square that day, but that wasn't the full picture.

In time it would all make sense.

He would have to play along with their game a while longer, he decided; now even keener to know who *Hilda* really was.

If she *was* working for who he suspected; even on their behalf, he might be able to glean or extract from her a clearer picture of what really took place that morning as well as clarify the strange things going on around him.

The 4th Bomb

At the end of a long day Daniel sat at home on his PC, sifting through images of the aftermath in Tavistock Square.

He had downloaded nearly 200 pictures from the Internet so far, in an attempt to piece together the crime scene.

He viewed images of the desolate bus, an abandoned black taxi, a blue lorry and the white Kingstar van.

He cast his eye over pictures of horrified people in stunned shock as rucksack carrying men rushed forward, pulling the dying from the wreckage without a hint of emotion.

Their lightning reaction so soon after the blast had been suspicious. A picture showed a tall gangly workman in a black donkey jacket, blue jeans and yellow hardhat securing the bus's perimeter. Later shots showed him motioning wildly, ordering uniformed police officers to and fro in the bus bombs immediate aftermath.

Daniel felt a pang upon staring at one image in particular.

It was an image of a disfigured body lying on the cold grey of Tavistock Square. He magnified it and scrutinised it closer.

It was visual confirmation, showing what remained of the blue and white shirt and the grey suit he saw Christian wearing at Euston station after 9am.

It showed the terrible damage wrought on his body by the blast. The injuries corresponded with him being seated on the *right-hand* side at the rear of the upper deck.

What gave clues to his proximity to the seat of the blast were images showing how those seated on the *left-hand* side at the rear of the upper-deck had been caught in the eye of the blast.

It was their blood that had been spattered over the white walls of the British Medical Association and their remains that required painstaking forensic work prior to identification.

According to reports in the newspaper 'sources' had stated Christian had died in the Piccadilly line train bombing, but the image in front of him proved that to be a monstrous lie.

The stunning realisation added a new dimension to Daniel's search for facts. He pondered for a moment, knowing that the *reason* for this lie was even more intriguing than the lie itself.

Initially the intelligence and security services' interest in him had been understandable, after all he was aboard the bus and they were hunting a mastermind or accomplices, but after they had 4 suspects the continued surveillance hadn't made sense.

It was strange how in the days following 7/7 he felt that his home and movements were being monitored. Now he had to assume they were also eavesdropping his phone calls.

That meant anyone he contacted or spoke to must have been placed under scrutiny and the calls he made immediately after the bombings to family confirming he was okay and later to friends including Brian *must* have been monitored.

He remembered telling Brian he was on the bombed bus the Saturday night when they went out clubbing, then on Sunday Brian rung him saying that Christian and his car were missing.

It wasn't until July 15th that the investigators told Christian's family that he died in the Piccadilly line blast, 8 days later.

Interestingly, that was the same length of time it took to retrieve all the dead bodies from the Piccadilly line bombing.

It that long because it had been a laborious task retrieving all the dead as the Piccadilly blast occurred in one of London's deepest and most narrow underground tunnels.

Once they had the final death toll, someone *inside* the investigation began the cover-up by placing Christian's body among the Piccadilly victims. Daniel knew this because he suspected *when* and *how* they could have identified Christian.

He remembered back to Sunday July 10th. Brian rung him to ask if he knew what Christian had been wearing that day.

Daniel now realised that Brian had been *told* to call him by the intelligence officer masquerading as a police liaison officer who wanted to find out how much he knew.

The 4th Bomb

The investigators have identified Christian by his driver's license to move his car on the *day* of the bombings.

This suggested that the cover-up actually began on 7/7 because if Christian *had* died on the Piccadilly line it would have taken days to identify him by his driver's license. This massive lie required the collusion of multiple agencies to carry out but the trail the cover-up left was *itself* proof of a cover-up!

(i)   Intelligence operatives whitewashing him out of the investigation by preventing him from making a statement during the investigation

(ii)   Operatives keeping him under surveillance, monitoring who he met or contacted

(iii)   Investigators responsible for the cover-up moving bodies and details around to bury the truth

(iv)   Media contacts falsifying information *intelligence sources* have supplied to support the cover-up.

A big discrepancy in the cover-up was the speed with which each bomb's fatalities were reported. Six were confirmed in the Edgware bomb and seven at Aldgate by noon on July 7th.

A number of dead were reported in the Piccadilly line bombing but only *two* fatalities were reported from the bus that day.

The next afternoon *sources* admitted that 14 died on the bus.

What was strange was that all the bus victims bodies had been removed well *before* forensics investigators arrived in their white PVC suits to comb the square around noon on July 7th.

So why was there a delay in reporting the number of fatalities from the 4th bomb which occurred *over-ground* on a bus?

Because the 4th bomb did not go according to plan and they needed to get their *story* straight before it could be released.

Casting his mind back, Daniel mulled over the sequence of events. It was strange how the facts were slowly beginning to reveal themselves and fall into place.

He could feel it; things were developing, moving around him. Things that he could not escape from, just like the bus blast.

The task that remained was like a web search.

All he had to do now was to ask the right questions in order for it to return the right answers; questions that no-one in the media or investigation was willing or capable of asking.

That moment of clarity, he thought, just that one moment of clarity, he knew it was somewhere within him.

It was the glint he recognised in his reflection as warm water dissolved the stain of those murdered from his hands minutes after the blast. The grand deceit had yet to take shape then, but now it was fully formed and ready to be exposed.

The clock ticked towards the wee hours of the morning.

The name *Hilda Edionseri* had drawn a blank in search engines.

Who was she? Daniel asked. What was her purpose, her job? Who were her contacts, friends and acquaintances? He wanted anything paper or digital verifying something, anything about her. He didn't have much luck so he tried *Witan Jardine*, the name of the agency she took him to. It was based in Holborn around the corner from the Ministry Of Defence HQ one page said. Daniel recalled its unassuming frontage and how once inside he noted the small cubicles they were led past that curiously had *ears* moulded into the walls. Other links relating to Witan Jardines recruitment role in the provision of staff in the areas of Public Finance Initiatives, the Ministry of Defence and government sector finance sprang up.

Later he wondered whether the agency was linked or indeed owned by the M.O.D, as his tired head flopped onto his pillow. He yawned. Maybe it would just be quicker to pay Hilda an unannounced visit to ask her, he thought, drifting off to sleep.

At work the next day he used the landline to dial the number he got from Witan Jardine's website.

'Good morning, I'm wondering if you can help me?'

'I've an appointment with a Miss Edionseri later this afternoon. Could you tell me the nearest station to your establishment?'

'Moorgate, on the northern line' the telephonist replied.

'Oh many thanks, and er, which floor will I need?'

'Er, she's on third floor' replied the telephonist, but when you arrive wait in reception and she'll be informed on your arrival.'

That afternoon he went down to Moorgate to visit the building where Hilda said she worked. He arrived at 13-15 Moorgate, the offices of the Arab Bank Plc. One of the links he found in his web search the previous night was a document showing that the Financial Action Task Force; a department the Ministry Of Defense set-up to counter international money laundering had audited and monitored many accounts the bank held.

The banks links throughout the Middle East meant it came in for close scrutiny in the wake of the 9-11 attacks where the funding of Islamic terrorist networks was targeted.

It kind of made sense, Daniel thought, walking up the steps. Witan Jardine recruited just the type of high calibre accountancy candidate's and finance professionals capable of mounting investigations into audit trails. Was Hilda a finance professional? He doubted it somehow, the way she was always borrowing a few quid here and there suggested otherwise.

Daniel entered the building and walked across its marble floor. The reception desk was unmanned.

The security guard must have been on lunch and the woman who turned him away on a previous occasion saying that Hilda was at a client meeting was nowhere to be seen.

He squeezed past the turnstile and pushed a button calling the lift. When its doors slid open a woman confronted him.

She smiled. Daniel smiled in return as she stepped out; a smile that suggested all was well.

On the 3rd floor he exited. If anyone asked, he was lost, looking for the gent's restroom, he told himself.

He took in his surroundings. It was unerringly quiet. *Too quiet.*

No one appeared to be home. He peered through the glass panel in doors all along the corridor till he came to a stairwell. Surely, the entire floor can't have all gone to lunch, he thought. He retraced his steps and checked the rooms in the opposite direction. After a full circuit of the 3rd floor he could safely report there was nothing but piles of boxes and stacks of chairs in most of the rooms. Other rooms stood empty.

The entire floor served as a storage space for office furniture.

There was no sign of activity at all, let alone Hilda.

She failed to get the benefit of doubt on this occasion. Now it turns out she didn't even work where she said she worked.

Daniel let out a sigh upon seeing without the myopia that tends to be prerequisite if romance is to bloom.

Everything Hilda told him about herself failed to stand up to any kind of scrutiny.

Five meals, 3 dates, 2 abortive dates and 1 night together was the final tally. Now he would to devise a final test, one pushing the burden of proof beyond any doubt, revealing who she was employed by before he employed the meanest and most cruel way of dumping her.

He got back in the lift and came out on the ground floor.

Walking briskly out he thanked the lady in reception as he left. She looked up with a slightly perplexed expression before returning to her magazine. As he headed back to the office he imagined memorable ways to dump her. Maybe he would arrange to meet her on a wonderful date in a really fancy spot in the West End then dump her by text at the appointed hour like a greedy executive culling employees. Yes, maybe that might be fitting, he thought, recalling the amount of messages he'd left on her voicemail that had gone unanswered.

By the time he arrived back at his desk he had simmered down a few levels. Common sense told him he had to do more than just get back at Hilda. Hilda had been placed in front of him. She was a piece of bait, a honey trap.

What he was embroiled in was way bigger than her. It was bigger than him… and it was also way *way* bigger than *them*.

Whatever he could unearth about her would reveal more about what it was he was at the centre of, so playing dumb and playing along with it for a while could prove useful.

There was a flipside though. If Hilda was playing dumb and she suspected he *knew* she was acting. It might make the shadowy game being played by those pulling her strings more dangerous, but that was a risk he was willing to take.

It was Thursday in late September, the week after he finished his consultancy role at the company in Old Street.

Tonight would make up for the leaving do that was scaled back to a swift pint in the pub across the road from work.

They would meet up for a memorable night out on the town.

It was a night where Oliviere's taste for the finer things in life, like cheesecake and the many cocktails on offer in London's glitzy bars combined with Daniel's extensive knowledge of the London club scene.

He made sure the patio doors were locked then went to check the skylights in the upstairs bathroom was shut before he left.

For a moment he knelt down on the floor, searching around on the tiled floor.

Right in the corner where dust had accumulated he found precisely what he was looking for. He picked it up and blew the dust off a single golden strand of hair that was about 5 inches in length. It belonged to Elizabeth, who his ex-lodger a few months before. Strands of her hair had been turning up in his Dyson vacuum cleaner long after she'd returned to Marseilles in her native France. It fitted the job perfectly.

In the next room his PC's gentle hum reduced to silence as he put it into stand-by mode.

He straightened out the items sitting on a shelving unit and took a reel of cello tape from a drawer.

Carefully he surveyed the room a final time then shut the door. Holding the strand of hair across the top right-hand corner of the door, carefully securing it in place at each end with two small bits of tape and with that Daniel left his apartment to go chase the blues away and paint the town red in equal measure.

At around 4:00am the following morning Daniel returned home exhausted after a raucous round of clubbing.

He removed the shoes from his aching feet and stumbled into the en-suite bathroom fighting off slumber. After a quick brush of his teeth, he squeezed a tube of facial scrub.

'Dammit' he muttered. It had given up its last.

He tossed the empty tube into the bin and wearily climbed the stairs to retrieve another from the upstairs bathroom.

He felt a sudden pang of alarm and froze. His heart quickened. Its pounding throbbed audibly in his head.

The office door stood ajar.

Cautiously he continued up, clambering for an explanation.

At the top he stopped to examine the strand of hair he'd placed across the door. The golden seal had been broken.

He slowly pushed the office door fully open and looked for signs anything was out of place as he entered.

Not only was his computer screen on, but it was logged in and the web browser open. This was strange because his PC automatically locked after 15 minutes of inactivity, then it would need a password re-entered to access it further.

As Daniel checked the bathroom and spare bedroom for any sign of intrusion his mind raced, trying to think through the haze of tiredness. He'd meticulously set the trap after Oliviere phoned him to confirm what time they'd meet up.

He did it after becoming suspicious when he came home and suspected a few things were out of place the last time Oliviere called him and they went for a curry at a local restaurant.

Daniel yawned. His eyelids were heavy. It was too much to worry about at this time of the morning. He needed sleep.

He went back downstairs and placed his key in the front door's keyhole. He turned it at a 90-degree angle in the lock preventing any other key or implement from being inserted, as he did each night, the last act before his head crashed against his pillow, leaving the searching questions for another day.

III

The Truth Will Set You Free

~Chapter 13~

Hearts & Minds

He didn't catch much of the embittered message Hilda left on his voicemail. In it she mentioned something about how he would never find a woman as classy as her.

'Hah!' he scoffed contemptuously, consigning her memory to history with a swift press of the delete key. He had more pressing matters to be concerned with right now.

Foremost in his mind was finding a way of getting what he witnessed into the public domain, to get the truth out there, but how?

The national newspapers he approached in July had all turned him away except for The Sunday Mirror whose reporter asked him to identify an Asian teenager who was *never* aboard the bus as the bus bomber.

In a way not revealing what he saw to the unscrupulous and untrustworthy hack had worked out for the best, because even if he'd received press coverage, there was nothing preventing the truth from being drowned in a deluge of erroneous facts or lost in a sea of editorial changes.

But the truth could set him free, if only he could set *it* free.

Going public would cover his back, just like Peter Power had done on July 7th when Power admitted in BBC radio and TV interviews that his company, Visor Consultants had held 4 terror drills that morning around the same locations of the bombings. Coverage is what was needed, he thought, to begin counteracting the lies that had sprung up in the absence of any factual evidence. Once he'd done that, the next struggle was to be taken seriously and that requires evidence, then *nothing* could stop him. The only thing that could stop him was *him*.

The battle for hearts and minds mounted in the relative calm of southern Iraq appeared on his television regularly.

British soldiers handed out sweets to Iraqi children.

These images were in stark contrast to scenes at home where Islamaphobia was rife. The British media's crusade equated an entire faith with a set of fundamentalist beliefs.

Daniel watched, knowing the media salvos were mounted on lies; lies as devious as the one Tony Blair told, when he claimed weapons of mass destruction were 45 minutes from launch. Then, the halo of decency Britain long prided itself on slipped. On July 7th 2005 Daniel witnessed it come crashing to earth.

It shattered. Pieces floated to earth and lay amid the debris and dead on Tavistock Square. The iconic image of the shattered bus stood as a huge blemish on the British, one that would remain for evermore.

If he needed further proof to believe this evil cowardly act was *in* character, history reminded him. It was the British Empire that honed the practice of enacting *lucrative* atrocities, but now in the *new age* it was their own citizen's they were devouring.

Daniel groped around on the floor beside the couch and sipped the warm remnants of a half finished can of lager, nursing that familiar uneasy feeling. It was the same faint lingering voice a small part of him had hoped would've become distant with time, but it had grown louder. The inner force urging him not disregard his misgivings had grown stronger as reports stemming from the investigations continued to trickle out.

There were too many inaccuracies and lies about where Christian died and too many inconsistencies in the shifting account's of Richard Jones that were given a global audience.

The months of surveillance Daniel endured had confirmed what he'd known all along. It was the very same *knowing* that had made him feel uneasy about providing a police statement the day after the bombings. Why because he knew then what he could prove right now, *he'd seen who planted the bus bomb.*

Now all was being revealed, it was one man against injustice, his simple faith against the intelligence machinery.

The Internet was an easy way to get information into the public domain, but the odds were still stacked against him.

He would have to be prepared for a media onslaught from the traditional British media establishment, sections of which *must* have colluded in the wide-reaching press cover-up.

As the operatives could not succeed in scaring him off, attacks mounted in the media, intent on discrediting him, his word and integrity had to be expected.

What smears would be levelled at him? He already knew of their earlier attempts at digging for dirt on him after Oliviere, his work colleague admitted being questioned by intelligence officers back in August. They'd hoped to find he was involved in criminality of some kind, but their probing drew a blank.

'Why didn't you tell me?' Daniel had asked him.

'I don't know' replied Oliviere, with a Gallic shrug.

'Maybe itz nothing?' came the Frenchman's hopeful reply.

'Per-aps, maybe itz something bad you did a long time ago?' he suggested, offering a sympathetic facial gesture.

Daniel pondered for a moment. It was as he'd suspected.

'Maybe it's something bad *they did* not long ago' he replied.

He wasn't annoyed with Olivier who, when asked told him the truth as he expected the secret services to dig for any kind of dirt to smear him with. They had already done it to a tube survivor called Gary who lost a leg. They did it because he supported calls for a public enquiry into the 7/7 attacks.

They also discredited a lady who had worked at the BMA too.

On the morning of 7/7 British Medical Association employee Richmal Oates-Whitehead reported seeing an army bomb squad in the grounds of the BMA *before* the explosion. A few days later she was viciously smeared in national newspapers and accused of being a liar and a fantasist. Then 4 weeks later she was found dead in mysterious circumstances in her flat.

'Networking... organisations... in... London' he murmured.
He hit return. Of the host of links the search engine returned,
one resonated.
Clicking on it brought up a flash animated introductory screen.

Welcome To The EPN
The Executive and Professional Network site.

*The networking forum for professionals. Held on the 3rd Wednesday
of each month at The Market Bar in Crutched Friars lane, EC3.
Nearest tube - Aldgate.*

Hmm, a chance to schmooze with professionals from the world
of journalism, media and PR. It sounded like an ideal starting
point he thought, adding his email address to the mailing list.

The following Wednesday he made his way to the EPN
meeting in Aldgate. After changing tube he headed for the
circle line. On the platform he stared at the tube map
pretending to plot his journey. He was being followed.
A man had appeared on the platform. Daniel had caught his
glance out of the corner of his eye, just before he looked away a
fraction too late. Daniel kept a discreet eye on him as the sound
of an approaching train was heard.
He followed the passengers aboard once its doors opened.
He stood, holding a handrail, aware of where the man stood at
the other end of the carriage. As pips sounded, indicating the
doors were about to close, Daniel hopped off a split second
before they shut, leaving his intelligence officer aboard as the
tube moved off into the tunnel. He cautiously walked around
the empty platform looking for any other observers before
boarding one of the following trains.

A few stops later he exited Aldgate Station and crossed the busy road outside. A man standing on the corner reacted as he neared the other side of the road. Folding his newspaper the man sprang into action and tried to cross the road.

Daniel's steps quickened as the man was held up, waiting for busy traffic to pass. Down the road Daniel continued, barely managing to keep his brisk walk from becoming a canter.

As soon as he turned the corner he darted into the courtyard of the first building he came across. He made himself scarce, disappearing inside a doorway, past the reception desk and down a stairwell on the ground floor.

After a while he came back up stairs and poked a speculative head round the corner to the buildings entrance.

Quickly he jerked his head back. There was the operative standing in the building's doorway scanning left and right.

Surely the operative must have gone by now, Daniel thought after a period of time. He ventured out, leaving the companies premises and continued to the EPN venue, a few blocks away.

Five minutes later Daniel got another surprise.

He turned a corner and emerged in Crutched Friars Lane. About 50 metres ahead he saw the operative that had been pursuing him earlier.

He paused and watched the operative scurry past the venue. Once he was safely out of sight Daniel approached The Market Bar, wondering who might have known he was attending.

Were his work emails being monitored, as his home PC's broadband connection seemed to be? Maybe the bald guy in blue overalls who was digging around under his desk had something to do with it.

On entering he venue Daniel noticed a few things missing. Firstly there was no one on hand to collect his admission fee.

Not a promising start he thought as he went downstairs to have a nose around. He detected the smell of turpentine and the tins of paint he saw were further evidence that workmen had recently applied a fresh coat of paint to its walls.

He let out a sigh, realising he'd turned up for nothing, unless he wanted to lend a hand with the redecorating that was in progress.

'After all that!' he huffed, trudging back up the stairs, wondering why he hadn't received an email about the event's rescheduling?

By the time he rode down the escalators into the underground, Daniel's exasperation had been replaced with a sense of relief.

He had taken a more philosophical view of his wasted journey.

It had been a blessing that he hadn't made any contacts that day, when he was under close scrutiny of the security services.

It had also highlighted the fact that he had to be more cautious with the information trail he left when planning to meet people or visit different places, as there seemed to be more than one department of the secret services on his case.

~Chapter 14~

The Phantom Menace

It was on Tuesday the 20th of September, just before 9 AM.
That was the first time *they* contacted him. His Nokia rang.
Daniel raised his head and reached over grabbing it off the bedside cabinet. He held it up blinking at its display.
The caller ID was hidden. Ordinarily he would've let a call this early divert to voicemail, but since completing his role the week before, there was a chance it might be one of the IT job agencies he was registered with. The chance it was another one of the odd calls he'd been receiving over the past few weeks also crossed his mind but he answered it anyway.
'Hello?' said a male voice at the other end of the line.
'Hello', Daniel replied, still yawning.
'Yes, I'm calling from the PSR agency, enquiring as to whether you are currently available for I.T work?'
'Er, yeah, what kind of role is it?' Daniel asked, still half asleep.
'Well the details of the job are a bit sketchy at the moment, but can I get you to send me a copy of your CV?' the caller asked.
'Okay' Daniel replied, as he rubbed the sleep out of his eyes.
'And can I have your email address?' the caller asked.
'Er… Daniel @ smartmode.com' came the deliberately wrong address as Daniel asked how an agency could have the mobile number on his CV but not have the email address printed on it.
'Um sorry, could you spell that again?' asked the voice.
'Er… no' Daniel replied having never heard of, or registered with an agency called PSR. A round of chuckles he heard in the background confirmed his suspicions.

'You're a bunch of pussies!' Daniel hissed, realising it was the group of operatives, the same ones assigned to monitor his movements, activities and contacts.

Realising the game was up, the caller hung-up.

So they were checking up on him. They had got lazy and now resorted to ascertaining his daily whereabouts the easy way, *by phone*, now that he no longer followed the predictable pattern of going to and from a regular place of employment.

Daniel's head fell back and hit the pillow with a sigh.

He dozed a while longer in thought. The call had told him more about the type of people he was up against and their seemingly ad hoc *Modus Operandi*.

If they were based at Enfield police station as he suspected, it would be handy when he'd gathered enough evidence to file a police complaint against them. The call also told him they didn't take him seriously, which wasn't such a bad thing. In fact it was probably a good thing, he thought, stifling a yawn.

~

He had enough time to reflect on their activities and behaviour. Somehow the intended two weeks off work spent trying to get over the harrowing events of July stretched into two months. This time was largely spent half-heartedly looking for work and lounging around his apartment.

The calendar ticked over into November.

Still no authority had contacted him in relation to the 7/7 investigations despite his two calls to the anti-terror hotline.

His recuperation was not helped by the ongoing surveillance, which seemed to escalate from around the time he finished work in September. He'd endured their scrutiny for 3 months and tension was mounting, but now he didn't find it frustrating any more. Something else had kicked in, something that went back, way back, something deep inside his being.

While the operatives were watching him, he was watching them and as they probed him, he too was probing them.

They had succeeded in helping him build-up a picture of what they were about and now he fully understood their game.

Their tactics were more cat and mouse than cloak and dagger.

It was a waiting game they played, a waiting and watching game. They had employed delaying tactics, designed to keep him away from the press and out of the media picture where what he witnessed would expose the real terrorists.

Their continued surveillance made it clear that he was considered a threat, but a threat to whom?

A threat to *them*, because of what he witnessed that day.

Maybe they didn't understand the way things worked in the new age, the information age. *The Aquarian age*, when the world entered a time of clarity, where evil could no longer hide, so evil had to be perpetrated in the full glare of publicity, *bold and brilliant*, right in front of peoples eyes *then* denied and concealed beneath media lies.

Daniel knew he would respond. Time would be the master.

Then how long till Eliza Mannigham-Buller, the head of MI5 handed in her resignation? And how long until D.A.C Peter Clarke head of the 7/7 cover-up was reshuffled?

How many arrests on the back of media lies would be announced in the bus bomb investigation, long after they'd claimed teenager Hasib Hussain was the bus bomber?

Daniel wondered all these things as he viewed an image he took of the man on the Victoria line tube on his PC.

He got a rush of adrenaline just viewing it; reliving the moment the operative stared downwards to avoid his confrontational glare before hurrying off at the next stop *in fear*.

Fear of what, him? The truth? Or was it just an inherent fear of an African man?

How much had the operative actually known about him? Daniel wondered as he uploaded the image. He posted it on the Ligali thread he'd documented his numerous encounters on. Recently he'd spent a lot of time on the boards of its forum.

It wasn't *Enemy Of The State*, he replied in response to one astonished member's post. It was all very real and if he could prove it to Ligali's moderators it would reach the 17,000 subscribers to their monthly newsletter.

He hoped this wider exposure would form part of his strategy. *Fighting secrecy with publicity.*

His earlier attempts at relaying what he witnessed taught him not to present all the information in one go, so on the Ligali thread he released the details gradually. That way he would avoid the funny looks and 101 questions that followed, as people attempt to reconcile it with what they already *thought* they knew.

However, this method of gradual dissemination was not making him popular among all forum members.

Some became highly skeptical of this tact, posing one accusing question after the other, while others played a *watching and waiting* game, especially one new arrival to the forum Daniel noticed using the provocatively named avatar 'Agent'.

~

Inevitably negative responses began to appear on the thread casting doubt as to how he could have possibly survived the bomb blast if he'd been on the bus.

Stung by this Daniel responded by uploading a picture he took of his grey shirt stained with bus victim's blood, hoping it would be enough proof to allay the doubters misgivings, as he needed to keep the Ligali members onside.

The 4th Bomb

Later that afternoon Daniel found a new post from *Agent* on his thread. Surprisingly it supported the plausibility surviving the blast and did so with information of a highly technical nature.

http://www.Ligali.org/forums/ index.php?showtopic=671		
Member: Agent **Group:** Visitor	**Posted:**	Dec 4th 2005, 11.06 PM

It's possible to survive a bomb blast from just feet away.
One bloke on the Picadilly line, was stood only 4 feet away from the bomber and survived. It really does depend on the blast, which way you're facing etc. (If you are facing the wrong direction, the blast goes into your mouth, down your windpipe and bursts your lungs, killing you) or on the other hand, you can just catch a more powerful part of the blast and be blown to bits.

The details were quite revealing. The in-depth knowledge *Agent* divulged about bomb blast injuries indicated to Daniel that he may have some involvement with the army or explosives somehow. The average Joe wouldn't have such in depth knowledge of the effects of explosives.

Even though the response backed his claims, Daniel suspected *Agent's* response was only because the more doubts forum members raised with his witness account, the more information would have released to prove he *was* on the bus and this was information *Agent* and didn't want getting out.

His post was an actually effort to gag him, just like the group of men keeping him under surveillance who'd succeeded in containing his story by *whitewashing* him out of the investigation and media.

Daniel paused for a moment after re-reading *Agent's* post.

Had *Agent* just explained why the bus driver leant out of the window the moment before detonation?

The next day when Daniel checked the thread for any updates and found Agent had posted another response.

http://www.Ligali.org/forums/ index.php?showtopic=671		
Member: Agent	**Posted:**	Dec 6th 2005,
Group: Visitor		06.58 PM

Daniel,

A number of years ago, a friend of mine who's a mini-cab driver was given a job to pick up a package and take it from one address to the other. He dropped of the package at its destination and thought nothing of it. Driving down the new Kent road, a whole load of cars sprang out in front of him, police jumped out with every form of gun you could think of.

He was stripped and put into a forensic suite and found himself in Paddington Green faster than you can say

"We the IRA have kidnapped a wife of top govt advisor and we want £250,000 or she get's it".

You see, it was the IRA that phoned the cab office with the job to pick up the money.

Now. My poor friend was under survelance for a long, long time. Yep it drove him up the wall. It drove him nuts.

It was a good 3 months before he thinks they stopped trailing him around all over the place.

Sorry to hear of your problems, but that's the way it is. They will eventually leave you alone once they realise you ain't a threat. I would not goad them or do anything, which would keep them interested in you. At least you survived the bomb! Good luck.

P.S Aren't you really known as "Dibbs"?

At least he survived the bomb? Hmm, Daniel thought.

Was *Agent* now *excusing* the ongoing surveillance or even making some kind of a veiled *apology* for the bombing?

The 4th Bomb

The name *Dibbs* rung a bell, Daniel thought as he typed a short conciliatory toned response to Agent's post.

http://www.Ligali.org/forums/ index.php?showtopic=671		
Member: Daniel	**Posted:**	Dec 5th 2005,
Group: Member		10.06 AM

@Agent, I am not or never have been known as Dibbs.
Is this Dibbs someone in the criminal fraternity you came across in the course of your duties?? :)

In fact Dibbs was a nickname inspired by a member of a popular rap group called The Wu-Tang Clan that his teenage brother adopted during a spell as part of a fledgling rap group. The one release he'd had was from the custody of a South London police station after being stopped with a group of hoodie wearing teenage friends a few years before.

As his younger brother was a minor Daniel attended the station and signed a document for the release of *Dibbs*, the first name that popped into his brother's head when questioned by the arresting officers.

By mentioning the name *Dibbs*, *Agent* confirmed he had access to police records, re-affirming Daniel's belief that various agencies were colluding at Enfield Town police station.

But which agency were *Agent* and the other operatives keeping him under surveillance working for? He wondered.

He could vaguely recall a news article from a paper a while back. Daniel went upstairs and returned with a worn copy of *The Sun* newspaper dated July 8th 2005.

In it was a report saying 550 *Special Reconnaissance Regiment* operatives had been drafted in to support the 2200 detectives with the anti-terrorist investigation into the 7/7 attacks.

Interesting, Daniel thought as he Googled SRR.

The Special Reconnaissance Regiment agent's surveillance skills were honed spying on the IRA in Northern Ireland. Formed from was the 14th regiment, the 550 strong SRR are specialists in covert surveillance, phone taps, tailing suspects and secret video recording and they were helping MI5 watch suspect terror cells.
Every agent is highly trained in breaking into houses, searching properties and leaving no sign that they have been there.
They are armed and experts in close combat.

Experts in close combat, eh? What the newspaper said tied in neatly with what *Agent* revealed about his *friends* in the army. His apparent explosives knowledge tallied with SRR's murky operations against the IRA in Northern Ireland led by their Director Jonathan Evans.

Rubbing the light stubble covering his chin Daniel reflected.
SRR… surveillance. On occasions his predicament made him wary about his safety. In unguarded moments the host of '*what ifs*' that plagued him would launch baser thoughts, more concerned with *survival.*
What if… *he hadn't left Tavistock Square in Hilda's company?*
What if… *he'd returned alone to his flat on the night of July the 7th?*
He slid open the patio door and stepped out onto the balcony.
It was a nice day but his outlook seemed gloomier than ever.
Still, he would deal with what happened whatever the consequences because they were choices he'd made long ago, they were based on morals and values he held.
He looked blankly across the flat tarmac roof of the vacant offices adjacent to his apartment, swirling deep in thought.
We choose things, but sometimes *things* choose us.

Daniel walked through Enfield Town shopping centre. Outside it he turned left to cross Church Street when he saw the face of a stranger that seemed familiar. Then it came back to him.

It was the man in the MPV on the Saturday morning after 7/7. The very same one who'd been watching him by the paper stand the day the press introduced Hasib Hussain as the bus bomber. This was the operative he'd spotted on at least 4 occasions. He was standing by the NatWest Bank on the corner in a blue t-shirt, a navy blue baseball cap and dark sunglasses, but today something differed about his behavior.

Whereas on previous occasions he'd avoided confrontation content to stalk from a distance, now it was as though he wanted Daniel to know he was under surveillance because as soon as he caught Daniel's attention he performed an abrupt 180-degree turn and headed off towards Enfield Town station.

The frustration rose in Daniel's chest. He didn't have to put up with this? He thought, watching the man walk briskly away. Suddenly Daniel broke into a jog, seizing his chance to turn the tables. He pulled out his cameraphone and darted past shoppers after him. The operative may have sensed the strides of an 6'3" African male lumbering up behind him.

In a few strides Daniel was alongside him, holding his camera phone point-blank at the side of the man's head.

As he took a hesitant glance it made an audible click, capturing the man's facial expression. Trying not to betray fear he kept walking as if totally oblivious to the fact that a camera was still held centimetres from his skull. Daniel slowed down and let the operative scurry off. If it's a reaction they want, he wasn't going to give them the pleasure and there wasn't much he else he could do within the confines of legality.

The image would provide more evidence for his IPCC claim, he thought, studying the frail look of uncertainty on the man's face his Nokia captured. Fear was definitely a two way street.

As soon as he returned to his apartment Daniel connected a cable and uploaded the image from the phone to his computer. There was a bit of camera shudder but the man's features were recognisable. He printed two A4 copies noting the time, date and location it was taken on each.

One he pinned beside pictures of other operatives on the wall of his office, the other he put in a box of newspaper clippings and notes he'd kept.

He took the box downstairs and there he arranged the A4 prints of all the operatives he'd taken on the rug in the lounge.

After studying them for some time he realised he could see definite pattern emerging.

He had encountered different kinds of intelligence operatives. Each seemed to have their own M.O and general appearance; even their attitude and approach differed.

The differences between them were stark enough for Daniel to be able to separate them into 3 distinct classes.

The first group he identified as MI5 intelligence officers.

This group included the male and female couple that showed up in the pub in Holborn immediately after the bus bomb and the chap who was sitting upstairs in the pub in Moorgate where he'd arranged to meet Hilda, then again snooping around his office a day after. They were all aged around their late twenties possibly early thirties.

Daniel could tell they bought into the serving queen and country line believing what they were doing was vital at a time of great peril with 45 minutes from WMD and all.

They were well presented probably thought they were *real* 007 material. *Laughable.* Information must clearly have been on a *need to know* basis for them, because their probing had been strictly covert and on the occasions he had '*made*' them they had quickly backed away regarding him with surprise and a great deal of caution.

By contrast the second group were almost the exact opposite.

They were either SO13, SO15, Anti-Terror branch or possibly members of Scotland Yard's Counter-Terror squad.

They were more aggressive and confrontational; similar to a few he'd seen in Tavistock Square in the immediate aftermath.

He had come into contact with one of them on two occasions in Enfield. Once while he was walking to Enfield civic centre situated next door to Enfield Town Police station.

Ahead a skin-headed, tall, gangly looking man approached and as they passed the man threw him a hateful stare.

Daniel remembered glancing back at him wondering what the queer look was for, only to find the man had turned round and stood there glowering at him. He recognised the menace in his face. He had at the wheel of a white van that chased him as he sat aboard a bus going to Wood Green one morning.

He was one of the government goons, a real psychopath, selected for their willingness to commit acts of murderous thuggery. They enjoyed looking mean and bearing firearms.

Their pugnacious, threatening demeanour and swagger told Daniel it was an ego thing with them.

The third and most visible group he came across were the Special Reconnaissance Regiment operatives (SRR).

July's newspapers spoke of them in the hastily convened COBRA meeting deep beneath Whitehall on the morning of 7/7 where the British leaders and security chiefs organised the response to the bombings.

Daniel knew his tormentors were part of that response.

The SRR, they were the ones responsible for the round-the-clock surveillance. The Internet had brought up a raft of facts on them and their regiments history.

The Special Reconnaissance Regiment was made up a group of British Military who had mounted covert surveillance and monitoring operations in Northern Ireland against the IRA as part of the secretive 14th regiment up until May 2005 when they were transferred to a base on the U.K mainland in Hereford where the S.A.S were also based.

One significant difference Daniel noticed was that the SRR were all older, aged in their forties. Maybe the harsh environs they'd operated made in them appear older.

They were discernable as they had the weathered slightly shabby appearance of guys who wouldn't look out of place queuing for soup. He had noticed them waiting around aimlessly in underground stations, loitering in shopping centres or standing on public transport, but this was London, *his* hometown, a bustling metropolis, not some laidback provincial town in Northern Ireland. In London everyone had somewhere to be and something to do, *in a hurry*.

Many a time it was the operative's lack of such a focus or purpose that highlighted them, making them stick out like sore thumbs.

On one occasion he'd been ambling along Chancery Lane when he turned into the entrance of a building to ask the security guard in reception for directions.

'I'm looking for the Independent Police Complaints Commission headquarters in Holborn' he'd asked.

He thanked the guard for his help and on the way out almost collided with a man who seemed to spring from nowhere.

Maybe it was the man's attire, a bit too shabby for the city that gave Daniel an inkling, but what really marked him out for further scrutiny was the slight look of surprise on his face as Daniel held the door open and stepped aside to allow the man to enter before he walked away. Daniel picked up the pace hurrying some way then darting into a pub a few doors down door in a bid to confirm his suspicions.

Still being early the pub was empty. Its door squeaked open. Daniel's footsteps creaked across its old wooden floorboards.

The barman didn't even look up from what he was doing till a moment later when the squeal of the doors hinges was heard a second time. Daniel looked round. The same man who'd entered the building 20 seconds ago now entered the pub.

The barman looked up. His face bore a puzzled expression.

For an moment there was an awkward silence as the three men stood looking at each other.

'Where is the Gent's restroom?' Daniel asked, breaking the ice. The bartender sensed something wasn't right about the day's first customers but nodded towards the pub's rear without unfixing his gaze.

Daniel followed in the direction he motioned, leaving his mute pursuant in the barman's company. He turned a silver knob in the restroom. A powerful burst of water shot out into the basin. When it had filled he turned the tap off and stared into the basin, watching the water form a vortex as it drained away.

He looked up at the mirror in front of him and silently asked himself the question he'd asked at regular intervals since 7/7.

Am I losing my mind? This was clearly what their continued stalking was designed to do, but his emotional and mental resilience was something they had not reckoned on.

They could stop him talking to the press but they couldn't stop him making an IPCC complaint, he thought resolutely.

The water slurped down the plughole and disappeared with a final gurgle.

Maybe the operative had blended in with his surroundings and was sitting out there with a pint of whatever it was they drowned their sorrows in.

The presence of British Intelligence was hardly surprising as the pub was 15 minutes from the Ministry Of Defence HQ and up the road from the pub where he nearly had a 9mm drawn on him by a female MI5 officer.

Daniel returned to the pub to find the spook had vanished and soon he was sitting in a neatly appointed waiting area of the Independent Police Complaints building entering information on a form the receptionist handed him.

He got to the part requesting details about his background and wondered what kind of background information the operatives were given on him.

Were they aware he was a 7/7 survivor and witness to the bus bombing? How would it look if their activities and treatment of a survivor came to media attention?

He completed the form and as he waited recalled what the links in his online search revealed about SRR.

These were the men that had facilitated dark deeds in Northern Ireland at the behest of the British state.

Their former commander Jonathan Evans was currently fighting to prevent many of their evil acts from coming to light in the wake of the Northern Ireland power sharing agreement.

If these proven murderers already had the blood of innocents on their hands, what difference would his make?

~Chapter 15~

The Crux

It was the 4th bomb, the fourth and final explosion that blew the investigation into the attacks along a different course.

It failed to go off according to plan and when it did nearly an hour later, besides leaving many dead, it also left many odd threads hanging, threads Daniel saw as events unfolded before him that morning.

The crux of the matter was that Christian died on *the bus*, not the Piccadilly tube that morning and the young Muslim blamed for the bus bomb was among those murdered that day, *not* a suicide bomber.

These crucial details had been painstakingly concealed from the public by a cover-up carried out by those supposed to be handling the investigation.

It was supported by the widespread propagation of lies *sources* passed onto their contacts throughout the British media in an insidious form of state control.

Aside from the shambolic British Intelligence operation between Euston and Tavistock Square the other weak link in the cover-up that followed was their witness.

His name was given as Richard Jones, aged 61 who claimed to have seen Hasib Hussain aboard the bus dipping anxiously into a rucksack.

Daniel immediately knew that Jones, a white haired old man had not been on the bus's lower deck as he claimed in his first account so he followed the way Jones's accounts changed with interest. The number of discrepancies between the 1st, 2nd and 3rd versions of what Jones claimed to have seen confirmed the serious inaccuracies in each of his accounts.

By the time the forensics arrived in Tavistock Square to begin sifting through the debris for clues at noon that day the bodies of the dead had been removed.

They were taken to a place called the resilience mortuary.

An online search revealed that the *Resilience Mortuary* as it was called, was based at the HQ of the Honourable Artillery Company in the City of London, a few minutes walk from where Daniel worked at Old Street. Its large main hall was divided into four sections, one section for the victims of each of the 4 bomb blasts.

Daniel recalled how its tall wrought iron gates had a large plastic sheet erected over it and a row of agitated policemen appeared outside it as he returned from lunch days after 7/7. Now he realised what the fuss that day was about. It was about *him!* He'd rung alarms bells when he stopped and stared through the gates on Friday, the day *after* the bombings, as lorries delivering the dead turned to enter its grounds.

The website went further stating that the mortuary was formed in accordance with government guidelines established under the *London Mass Fatality Plan* – a plan devised to provide emergency capacity during crises with a high death toll.

'Now I see', Daniel realised, nodding slowly. It had taken time for the grey cloud of smoke that hung over the bus to disperse, but the dots were slowly but surely joining up. Things were becoming clearer, edging him closer to the truth behind what happened that day. On a notepad he wrote a definitive list of what he knew so far, starting with the initial statements made on the July 7th, given by the likes of Peter Power, Tony Blair, Deputy Assistant Commissioner Peter Clarke, Sir Ian Blair and last but not least, Richard Jones.

Their statements were issued following confirmation that 'power surges' were in fact bomb blasts, when the world was waiting for an unclear picture to settle and before the media's cloud of confusion began shrouding the skies 24 hours later.

In a BBC radio interview that morning Peter Power stated that his company Visor Consultants had been conducting terror drills at 3 tube stations and 1 train station at *nearly* the exact times and locations of the bombings. Now Daniel understood what Peter Power had meant by *nearly*. He referred to the 4th *train* bomb that for some reason became the 4th *bus* bomb.

On July 7th, hundreds of miles away at the G8 summit in Scotland a sombre faced Tony Blair gave a speech at noon calling the attacks the work of extremists.

The speed at which he arrived at his conclusions made Daniel call into question the relative speeds at which each of the bombs were reported. The number of dead at Aldgate and Edgware stations were confirmed early on, but the number of fatalities from the Piccadilly line tube and the bus in Tavistock Square were still sketchy at this point.

Strangely, the bus had been destroyed *above ground* yet the number of dead took longer to clarify, even though by noon, when the forensic teams arrived, the square had already been cleared of bodies.

Despite this, media sources reported only 2 fatalities, in the face of the wholesale carnage evident to all who'd passed Tavistock Square that morning.

Alongside initial newspaper reports of 2 fatalities on the bus was Richard Jones's initial account, detailing his sighting of a dark-skinned man dipping into a rucksack aboard the lower-deck minutes before the explosion. By the afternoon of Friday July 8th radio reports revised the number of dead from the bus to 14. From that point onwards Jones's story began to alter.

By the following week his account had changed again, paving the way for a theory that was to emerge, a theory surrounding a Muslim teenager named Hasib Hussain, whose image was captured on CCTV entering Kings Cross station just after 9.00am. This single image was deemed sufficient evidence for him to be labelled a *suicide bomber* responsible for the bus blast.

Daniel applied some logic. The initial blasts went off at 8:51am. If Hussain had been part of a suicide cell he would have died then. What points to him *not* being part of a terror cell or at least not being aware of what the trio were up to was when he attempted to call their mobile phones *after* 9am.

What is known is that Hussain was caught on CCTV waiting for someone that morning at a nearby McDonalds restaurant. This points to him unwittingly but conveniently placed on standby, a patsy perhaps?

If Hussain didn't die on the bus what became of him?

An Australian who'd been working in London reported that an Asian male was shot dead by police gunmen in Canary Wharf that same morning and his entire building were warned to keep away from the windows as there was a 'security scare'.

Two foreign websites reported it briefly before the deluge of other reports buried it. Daniel's search for any remnants of the story were fruitless, but still, there was absolutely no evidence Hasib Hussain was ever on the bus 30.

Another angle of investigation was the bomb itself. For some reason the 4th bomb changed its course, why? Newspapers said it was due to the Northern Line underground being shut at 7am that morning. Whatever the truth was, the bomb was left with nearly an hour to target something else or even *someone* else, someone who boarded the bus, perhaps.

Daniel launched his web browser. Within a few clicks, his stare lingered on a page bearing the faces of the bus bomb's victims.

In a separate browser window was a picture of Christian that had been on the web and featured in the national press.

Who could it have been… and *why*? He wondered, staring long and hard at each picture in turn wondering why those responsible for the investigation had led the public into believing that Christian died on the tube? What purpose did this *lie* serve? What had Christian ever done to anyone?

Anyone who knew Christian knew him as a man of integrity, who was always willing to help others. Daniel recalled when Christian had returned from a long stint in Ghana, West Africa doing voluntary work for a charitable organisation.

Was there a link of any sort? He wondered, scouring his memory. Something did ring a bell.

It was a report he'd heard a few months back. Daniel could recollect how his ears pricked up one morning on hearing a news report on the radio of another police shooting.

Most incidents of police shootings revolved around Operation Trident; Scotland Yard's taskforce focusing on the black community, but the report went on to say it was a young man who worked for a charity in Ghana… an Englishman, if he recalled correctly. He punched some words into the Google search bar and clicked on a link it returned.

The dead mans name was Simon Murden, aged 26 who'd lived in Yorkshire. He worked for the 'And Albert Foundation', a charity his father founded in the 1980's.

His death briefly made the headlines on the 22nd March 2005 the day he was shot dead by armed police. This was exactly 4 months before armed police shot Jean Charles de Menezes on July 22nd at Stockwell, shooting him 7 times in the head.

Daniel began taking down notes. Murden had been driving his blue van on his way to work that morning, three weeks after returning from doing some charity work in Ghana.

A chase of some sort ensued before a stand-off took place and he was shot dead.

There were many startling parallels with the killing of the Brazilian in July. As in the De Menezes case, there were words attributed to an unknown bystander claiming that Simon, known to many as a sensitive, humorous and thoughtful individual, had been brandishing a gun-like implement.

This, according to the newspaper article had left the gunmen with '*no option*' but to shoot him.

Daniel found more reports on other websites where the word *gun-like* had been replaced with *blade-like*, but this was of little comfort to the deceased man's family who would later place their hopes in an IPCC inquiry into the circumstances surrounding his horrendous and senseless slaying.

Daniel recognised an all too familiar pattern in the Murden case with ones he'd been made aware in regions of Africa.

Murden may have been pressured by elements of MI6 working for the British Foreign Office's security department.

The Foreign Office needed *clean* people to do their bidding to advance their neo-colonialist agenda on the African continent.

Over the 20 years Simon's father's charity had operated, it had built-up a huge amount of goodwill and trust among its partners in 28 communities across Africa, assisting with sustainable development projects and fair-trade partnerships. Theirs was a trust and goodwill that the British government has *never* had in Africa, as history itself documents.

In more recent times the catastrophic record the British have in Africa has hindered their ability to influence or negotiate access to rich minerals resources across the continent.

Tony Blair's smiling new crusade to *save* Africa began with the setting up of the 'Commission For Africa' in 2004.

It was part of this agenda, the same agenda that hijacked Bob Geldof's Live8 concerts.

Sadly for the Murden family the Foreign Office routinely approached *decent, helpful* humanitarian workers and volunteers who've earned the trust of communities to serve state interests through the backdoor via so-called *Non-Governmental Organisation's* as Africa learns from the past and become wise to the rise in Britain's new colonialist activities.

And the Ghanaian connection was raised further still.

There was a connection to the attempted bombings that took place in London two weeks after 7/7 on the 21st of July.

The 4th Bomb

Manfo Kwaku Asiedu was the alleged 5th bomber. He wasn't much of a Jihadist though; apparently he got scared, hid his device in a park and was apprehended the very same day.

This was despite him not being flashed on television screens nationwide like the quartet caught on CCTV as they fled leaving their home-made devices to cause much alarm.

Even stranger was that Manfo Kwaku Asiedu was not the *so-called* 5th bombers real name. In fact it was the name of the son of Ghana's former head of Secret Services, who hurriedly appeared on national television in Ghana denying his son was a terrorist and it was a case of *taken* identity. Could he detect a whiff of a British Intelligence vendetta? Unsurprisingly the authorities put *Manfo* on trial separate from the other four.

A further search unearthed reports that Manfo was an African illegal immigrant who'd attempted to join the British army.

So how had he got involved with a martyrdom plot?

Daniel knew he would need to unearth more facts to prove the connection, but he was sure of one thing as he reviewed the timeline surrounding the disappearance of Christian's car; those involved in the 4th bombs cover-up messed-up *big-time.*

1. <u>Thurs 7th July: 9.47am</u> Bus blast - 2 fatalities reported
2. Christian's Mistubishi car goes missing that afternoon
3. His flat-mates find his car missing late that evening
4. <u>Friday 8th July pm</u> Bus bomb death toll is revised. 14 bus fatalities are reported dead that afternoon
5. <u>15th July</u> – Christian's family is notified of his death. This is a full <u>8 days</u> after he failed to return home
6. <u>Monday 18th July</u> ·Christian's face appears in the national press among the *Piccadilly tube* fatalities
7. <u>Friday August 5th</u> Brian rang saying *they* found his car the previous week parked in a street in Kings Cross.

How convenient! It gave Daniel the sense that the hurried re-organisation of evidence to support the lies had begun to fray.

What was Christian's car doing in Kings Cross? He wouldn't have driven from Walthamstow all the way into London. He took the Victoria line tube from Walthamstow to Kings Cross each day. Driving made no sense for a number of reasons.

1. It was much quicker and easier for him to take the Victoria Line tube to work as he did each morning.
2. It takes more than 90 minutes by car due to London's congested traffic. If he'd driven he would not have made his meeting on time.
3. It's more expensive. His car was found parked *inside* London's <u>congestion charge zone</u>, where an additional charge of £5 was payable for the day.

He felt a cold shiver of excitement. He was onto something groundbreaking. At last here was something solid. Evidence with a time-stamp, proof! The last point was the most telling.

It was a smoking gun because the congestion charge was payable by any vehicle entering London's central congestion zone between 7am and 7pm and Christian left home at 8am.

If his car *had* entered the congestion zone it would have been captured on congestion charge cameras and he would have had to pay the £5 toll by midnight. Failure to do so would have meant he was automatically issued with a £20 penalty charge notice as the registered owner of the vehicle.

The lack of either proves he *never* drove to King's Cross on the morning he died and even if he had for some bizarre reason decided to drive all the way to King's Cross, he would have *had* to have arrived there before 7:00am which was impossible as he left home in Walthamstow at 8am.

Either way, this proved Christian did not drive his car to King's Cross that day. So the question becomes, who did?

The answer to this question was no mystery to Daniel.

Assuming Christian kept his car keys in his pocket, like most people do, whoever moved his car and later left it in Kings Cross *must* have got the keys from someone involved in the clean-up of Tavistock Square that began around noon that day.

This was obvious. He'd seen it all as clear as day, except back then yet it didn't make sense. Now, with the evidence that had come to light, it did.

The hurried removal of Christian's car that day implicated those charged with *investigating* the bus bomb in the tampering and misappropriation of evidence. Who else could have known it was his car? Which organisation has the resources to gather and act on this information with such speed?

Daniel went over it again, just to be doubly sure.

A wallet with Christian's driving license found on him or among the debris would show his photo and car registration.

He knew it would also show that Christian fitted the description Richard Jones gave, of a *dark-skinned* man, just as Anthony Fatayi-Williams or he, himself would have.

But this information alone would not yield the precise location of Christian's car unless they had been trailing him.

Only one organisation had the resources to achieve this, the same organisation that could coordinate the cover-up and arrange the surveillance of a survivor.

The answer was British Intelligence.

Namely MI5, under the direction of Eliza-Manningham Buller.

Daniel was also struck by another small detail. How much had Brian known? He was embroiled in this through his association with Christian and himself. It was Brian who'd rang them both the week before, arranging to meet-up Monday at the Ion Bar's Salsa night. Brian rang again from Euston on Sunday 10th July, the day after he confided in him about being on the bombed bus during a night out in the West End. He'd been with Christian's flatmates Vanessa, Simone and Tameka in Kings Cross, out hanging-up missing posters and talking to the press that had descended on the area. When they were approached by a police liaison officer who questioned them and took the photos they had of Christian from them. Brian rang him again later to ask what Christian had been wearing, he told him. 'Yeah, a grey suit with a blue and white shirt and tie' he said.

But strangely Brian murmured something back about Christian wearing black.

Hmm, where was the logic in posing the question if he knew what Christian was wearing? Daniel thought a while later, feeling there had been something odd about the call, but Brian's suggestion that Christian wore black hadn't introduced any doubt in Daniel's mind if that had been his intention.

In retrospect he knew it was likely that the 'liaison officer' they met was involved in the cover-up and told Brian to pose that question so they could eavesdrop and learn how much his friend knew. The fact that intelligence officers were visiting anyone with even the remotest connection to him spoke volumes. Such was the reach of the state's machinery and its desperation. Still, Daniel knew the greater importance of Brian in all he was enduring. Brian was an enabling factor, a maven.

He was the link between Christian, himself and many others.

It had taught Daniel a few things about trust.

Real trust is to trust the good to be good, the loyal to remain loyal, to trust that liars will lie and trust that the evil would be consumed by their own evil deeds.

~Chapter 16~

Operation Tri-it den

The radio's muffled drone could be heard from his bedroom.
It helped drown out the phone conversation he made in the en-
suite bathroom.
The bathroom's smooth tiled walls and surfaces ensured there
was no place listening devices could have been hidden.
Since realising his apartment had been entered in his absence
this was a procedure he followed before making calls relating
to his future movements or intentions.
With a new SIM card in his phone he called the number he
received via the Ligali forum's private messaging facility to
confirm a meeting place and time. Daniel ended the call
thinking that using an intermediary to arrange the meeting
might suggest Toyin still had doubts about him and felt the
need to size him up first. Things were not turning out to be as
straightforward as Daniel had hoped. A lot hinged on this
meeting. Inclusion in Ligali's mail-out was vital, because if the
Ligali members didn't believe him, who would?

Days later Daniel stood outside a bookshop. The black woollen
hat on his head kept the crisp November chill at bay.
He felt a tenseness; as though unseen scrutinisers lurked
among the crowds of shoppers. After some time the waiting
and watching seemed to be adding to this feeling so he
retreated into the shop and wandered among its shelves of
books.
'Yeah, I'm there' Daniel said, when his mobile phone rang.
'Can you see the book shop?' he asked, peering out the shops
front windows.

'Yeah, be with you in a few' the caller answered.

Daniel came to the entrance and watched a light-skinned man with a wispy goatee beard on the other side of the road snap shut his phone and cross over.

He had dreadlocks contained in a peaked woolly hat.

As he got closer Daniel saw a *no justice, no peace* badge decorating his green army surplus anorak.

'It's Kamal right?' Daniel asked, briefly shaking his hand.

'Yeah safe' the man said nodding.

'Let's take a seat' he said.

'Here will do' he said, gesturing towards the soft seating in the bookshop's coffee area.

'Er, probably not' Daniel said warily, seeing as it was directly in the shop window in full view of anyone passing along Wood Green high street. The expression on Kamal's face the moment they first met had done little to settle the uneasy feeling he had earlier.

'So what happened to Toyin?' Daniel asked as they headed to a restaurant inside Wood Green shopping centre.

'Couldn't make it... busy' replied Kamal briskly.

Kamal rummaged around in his satchel when they sat down.

'Wanna drink?' Daniel offered.

'Er, no I'm alright' Kamal replied.

The waitress who took the order returned, placing a fizzy drink on the table in front of Daniel.

'Have you been a Ligali member long?' Daniel asked, slightly alarmed as Kamal untangled the wires of an Mp3 recorder.

'For a while' he replied, sounding a bit too vague for Daniel's liking. Sipping his drink Daniel waited for the Mp3 recorder to begin working and when it did the meeting commenced.

An hour or so later it had more or less concluded.

'Okay... um, yeah. I'll get back to um, Toyin and... we'll see what we can do.' Kamal said, sounding less positive than his continued nodding suggested.

The following Wednesday evening Daniel set in motion the other part of his plan. He slid the £5 entrance fee across the desk to a rather photogenic girl in The Market Bar and went downstairs where the sound of polite applause resounded.

He'd caught the tail end of a prize-winning journalist and author launching her new book. A busy murmur was heard as fledgling PR professionals and enterprise-minded attendees networked during the intermission.

He had timed it well, coming during the event's booze and schmooze section, precisely what he came here for.

Introductions were plentiful. A few faces were familiar.

The very outgoing girl still trying to get a PR firm off the ground, a few impeccably turned out guys bristling with entrepreneurial verve; the cut of their suits alone said they meant business.

Many were eager to impress by way of words, some were even interested to know what he did and where he worked. To some he was a writer, to others he was a researcher but to all he was full of questions, eager to know how they operated in their particular sphere of influence.

Daniel spotted a familiar character leaning up against the bar.

'Long time', the man said, nodding astutely.

'Chibu… it's been ages, what brings you here?' Daniel asked.

'Here with a friend, who helped organise the launch'

'You know the author?' replied Daniel, interested.

Chibu motioned to his left nonchalantly.

'Richard… this is Daniel, an old school mate of mine'

'Daniel, meet Richard, PR svengali and general mister fix-it.'

'Richard Adeshiyan' announced the stout African figure in a resolute tone.

Out shot a palm that shook Daniel's hand firmly.

'PR… interesting' Daniel said nodding.

'What are you drinking' he asked, pointing to the glass Chibu was holding.

After the bartender served the drinks Chibu took a few sips then seemed to lose interest in favour of fairer distractions.

'So you assisted with the book launch?' Daniel said, turning to Richard.

'Well, I set-up the whole thing, essentially.' Richard replied.

'PR… how interesting' said Daniel, nodding agreeably.

'I take it you're from a journalistic background then?'

'Yes, I used to work for The Voice newspaper' he replied.

'The Voice? Then you must have known the previous editor. She was a good friend of mine' said Daniel.

'I even contributed a small article for it once' he added.

'Oh? When… what was it about?' asked Richard, with a slightly surprised expression on learning Daniel had fraternised with his former boss.

'It was an exclusive report exposing police corruption in South London involving officers who ran a crack factory in Brixton.' Richard listened intently, nodding keenly as Daniel relayed the details.

'Did you know… I set-up a newspaper?' Richard asked.

'The New Nation newspaper…launched in 2000' he continued.

'Oh, maybe you still have some contacts there?' Daniel asked.

Over more drinks Richard's anecdotes and notable achievements flowed.

'I flew on the private jet of Nigerian Head of State, Sani Abacha when he flew to Switzerland, doing a newspaper article'

'Switzerland? For an article? Daniel said, sounding impressed.

'That's interesting because I'm doing another highly secret article coming out soon. Perhaps you know the kind of people I should be talking to? It's a bit hush-hush at the moment but if you have a card…?'

'Certainly' replied Richard. After momentarily fumbling around in his jacket pocket he handed Daniel a card.

'Give me a call. We'll work something out' he said, beaming.

'Definitely' replied Daniel, staring at the card's lettering.

When Daniel left the venue he was in a better mood than when he arrived. It was dark outside, but he was beginning to see a chink of light at the end of the long dark tunnel.

He ambled along to Liverpool Street and caught a train back to Enfield after what had been a very productive evening.

Richard was just the man he'd been on the lookout for, with just the right type of contacts he needed. His help, combined with Ligali's would hopefully give him enough coverage to get the truth out there.

The other part of his plan was proving to be less fruitful thus far. No one from Ligali had got back to him yet even though he had been told that someone would.

Daniel made his way to East London to attend a Ligali members meeting the following weekend hoping meeting face to face might help sway the decision they seemed to be deliberating over, as Ligali was an important part of his plan.

At the centre of his trident-shaped response was the website he was designing, that would release the facts and digital evidence at regular intervals. Media coverage would be provided with the help of Richard on one hand through the many established contacts he had and Ligali on the other, through their network of organisations and regular mailouts.

Daniel stared out of the bus window hoping the sceptics on the forum hadn't put paid to his plans.

At Edmonton Green he changed buses, boarding a single-decked 149 bus and took a seat near the centre as the bus began its journey. It proceeded through Tottenham, an area with a large African population onto Seven Sisters with its rich cultural mix.

Further on it came to a halt at a bus stop on Stamford Hill, an area where orthodox and Hasidic Jews in black hats could be seen making their way to the Jewish centres the area was known for. Among the recently arrived African immigrants, the elderly Muslim gentlemen and the young mums with their baby buggies Daniel took a cursory look at a solitary white man aboard the bus standing near it's centre doors.

Once Daniel had turned away it struck him.

He was one of the surveillance operatives! The same one he'd taken a snap of on the tube weeks ago. The man was recognisable by his large quiff-like plume of hair, which affected by male patterned balding on the sides.

Daniel looked again noting his chunky Adidas cross trainers and long quilted coat. Was his long coat concealing anything?

Daniel's mind flirted with the notion that someone may have tipped them off about his intention to attend the Ligali meeting, but how? He hadn't discussed anything specific in his private messages with Voo or Toyin and hadn't spoken of his intention to attend when Kamal made him aware of its details during their meeting. Daniel was still wondering when the 149 bus slowed as the road to Dalston became congested.

He looked over at the operative who looked away as the bus stood idling in busy traffic. He was all on his own with nowhere to go.

Daniel stood up quite suddenly, an act that seemed to raise either the stakes or the temperature as the operative reacted by unzipped his long quilted coat.

Maybe he was indicating he had nothing concealed under it.

Or he may have been preparing to draw something out if he felt the situation called for it. The operative returned a furtive glance as Daniel edged closer to where he stood.

Daniel leant against the window.

His hands were hidden in the front pockets of his hooded top.

The man used the back of his hand to mop the beads of perspiration appearing above his brow as the tension mounted. Unless British Intelligence had managed to recruit Somali immigrants, teenage mums or one of the Asian senior citizens sitting feet away totally oblivious to the confrontation there seemed to be no other operatives nearby.

A shot of adrenaline coursed through Daniel's system.

His fist tightened to a clench. If he wanted to go out in a blaze of fury, here was his opportunity, a dead cert.

For a moment he toyed with the idea, feeling an adrenaline rush surge through him, but he knew exploding in a burst of rage against the servant of cowards would be fruitless. It was the truth that was his strength. The truth was his priority.

It was the reason the *servicemen* trailed him. Monsters caught by their own evil. Caught that day in Tavistock Square.

Now he haunted them. They were restless, they wanted rid of the truth, they wanted rid of him.

Daniel stood revelling in the operative's edginess.

He wondered what was flashing through the operatives mind? Was he recalling the terrible fate of those who lost their lives aboard a bus?

Ulster this was not. Neither was it Herefordshire.

When would they realise they stuck out like sore thumbs in areas as culturally diverse as this?

It was no surprise that MI5 were on a recruitment drive to find Asians and blacks to *use* as their eyes and ears in multicultural communities.

The man Daniel looked upon seemed pitiful now, a small cog in the intelligence machinery. Doing a secretive job he did not appear to be relishing at the moment.

Just the two of us Daniel thought, taking a cumbersome step closer. The operative stepped away nervously muttering something under his breath as a camera phone took another snap of him.

By the time Daniel checked the image he'd taken the bus doors had swung open. The operative seized the opportunity to escape the bus's confines walking briskly away as Daniel eyed the memento of their encounter.

A couple of stops later Daniel got off. He surveyed Kingsland High Road in both directions.

After walking a short distance he entered an unassuming restaurant. It's door rattled as he pushed it open.

Inside he saw an elderly Caribbean gentlemen sitting on a chair near a staircase that led to a basement.

The old man's head bristled with flashes of silver streaks that he wore like a crown. He looked up, viewing the cagey customer with a spirited smile and a wizened gaze that recognised something in a new generation, in a new age, something he had seen a generation before.

Daniel attempted a smile as he passed down the stairs to a makeshift auditorium in the basement wondering how he'd be received after the furore his thread raised on the forum.

Downstairs he made the conscious decision to sit in the corner, two rows behind Kamal, who he saw sitting at the front near a projector.

As he pulled up the chair, Kamal glanced over his shoulder gaving him a shifty look as he sat down. Though his face bore a look of mistrust, he offered Daniel a greeting in the form of a silent nod.

Daniel met his gesture with an equally standoffish nod in return. He noted the same MP3 recording device around Kamal's neck that he had when they met in Wood Green.

He felt Kamal was untrustworthy then and was immediately reminded of this on seeing him today.

How close was Kamal to Toyin? Daniel wondered.

Who was to say the Ligali organisation hadn't come to the attention of the authorities or even had its own embedded informant?

As he sat listening to a debate Daniel felt his decision to withhold pertinent details till he met Toyin face to face had been vindicated.

The basement began to fill. The debate grew, becoming more spirited as members arrived.

Flashes of Kente cloth exchanged greetings with hair adorned with red, black and green beads.

Denim designs clashed wonderfully with colourful head wraps. African prints mingled with kaftans and Nike trainers.

Before long the room was abuzz as talkative members sat assembled while a group of children played noisily in the adjoining room.

'Sorry I'm late people!' announced Toyin, arriving in a blur of African print sweeping past those seated to the front.

'Are we waiting for anyone else?' he asked looking among the faces congregated.

'Okay, before we start, today's film's called *The Spook Who Sat By The Door.*'

'It's based on a novel written by Sam Greenlee that was hugely controversial when it was first released back in the 1970's. '

'It runs for an about an hour 40 minutes after which time we can begin the debate. Is everyone okay with that?

'Due to time constraints we'll do new member introductions before we begin the debate.'

'Oh, elder come, bless us with your presence!' Toyin said.

All those congregated including Daniel turned round.

The man he saw as he'd entered had come down the stairs. Pulling up a chair he assumed a similar position at the back from where he could oversee proceedings.

With a glint in his eye he sat among the burgeoning spirits, timeless, spawned from seeds of revolution he'd seen when he walked among giants.

The lights went down and the film commenced.

~Chapter 17~

Statement

Bursts of colour were met with shrieks of delight by those gathered around global landmarks. A tumultuous year had ended and a new one began. Daniel had reason to be thankful, but viewed the revelry onscreen with a sense of detachment.

The first week of 2006's highlight had been the sight of a Ford Mondeo trundling into view with Kieran Watson at the wheel. His face screwed up in a fit of rage as he accelerated past into the underground cark park, returning to empty his locker after being dismissed a week after Daniel uploaded footage of him had been to the forum. Daniel did it after realising it was Kieran who'd been updating *contacts* inside Enfield Town Police station on his daily comings and goings.

'You'll deserve what's coming to you!' shouted Kieran, angrily waving a fist out of the car window.

A satisfied sigh accompanied a mildly contented smirk as Daniel returned a mocking wave goodbye to the informer, savouring a moment he'd been looking forward to for a while.

Though a new year was upon him, the events of 2005 hadn't concluded with the year's end. Much remained unresolved.

7/7 was six months ago yet he still hadn't been contacted or interviewed by anyone from the investigation.

It made him feel his life was in limbo. What did the year ahead hold for him? He wondered, as he sat snacking on the remnants of festive foods in a belligerent mood.

He slouched back on the couch reviewing a DVD he recorded of the BBC and Channel 5 documentaries on his chosen subject, *the 7/7 attacks*. The first was entitled 'The Day The Bombs Came' and the other 'London - Under Attack'.

He was reviewing footage of a man in a grey shirt standing to the right of the bombed bus in the aftermath, he paused for a moment and rewound it again, playing it back frame-by-frame. The footage jerked slightly as the CCTV camera panned to the right zooming in on the figure looking left down Tavistock Square then back at two policemen standing across the road.

Whoever had been monitoring the grey-shirted man on CCTV camera *must* have monitored the bus explosion in its *entirety*.

Why would CCTV cameras in the Square suddenly begin working minutes after the bus exploded but not before?

The media had claimed all the CCTV cameras had not been working that day. This piece of footage proved otherwise.

Daniel reviewed it over and over, drawn back to the scene.

He had doubts that morning just as the man in the grey shirt in the footage appeared to have, doubts raised by the strange activities he'd seen following the blast. Daniel knew this because the man he was viewing onscreen was him.

He ejected the DVD and went upstairs.

After ripping the footage to his PC's hard drive he reviewed the clip once more.

Wait till they see this, he thought, logging onto the forum in an air of excited ness. It would be a final riposte to those who doubted or poured scorn on his claims. It was more compelling evidence backing up what he witnessed.

With a click on the upload button it was uploaded, there for all forum members, visitors, GCHQ and intelligence organisations worldwide to see.

By the second week of January the period Daniel had spent out of work, had the effect of edging him nearer to the truth.

He flicked through the diary in which he recorded details of his encounters with the security services and posed the question, had the surveillance run its course?

The last entry he'd made was in late December.

After flipping back a few pages back to previous weeks he suspected the hiatus might be due to a seasonal lull.

Perhaps the lack of activity indicated their budget had been spent or maybe their lack of success made their top brass pull the round-the-clock operation.

Daniel thought this might be the case by the way the odd phone calls and online encounters had increased markedly while the physical surveillance had tailed off since December.

Maybe they had finished with him and the days when he could walk down the street without casting a cautious eye would soon return, he thought, daydreaming momentarily.

Later that week Daniel's mobile phone rang.

'Hello, I'm calling from Yorkshire police' a female voice said.

'Oh? Go ahead' he said, activating the phones record function.

'Yes, I'm trying to get some correspondence out to you'

'It's for a vehicle with this telephone number on it. We need your company's address' she said in a Yorkshire accent.

'What company?' asked Daniel, somewhat bemused.

'*Your* company… Jumbo Freight'

'Err… I think you've got a wrong number' Daniel replied.

'Jumbo Freight doesn't ring a bell' he said, sounding confused.

'I don't have the wrong number, its *your* number printed on the back of the van' she insisted.

'Van… what van? You need to check your records… I don't have a van or any business up in Yorkshire!' Daniel replied, knowing Yorkshire was where the alleged *suicide-bombers* came from. Becoming increasingly agitated by the women's continued insistence he cut her off mid-sentence.

Whoever instigated the call would find it had backfired *seriously*. He'd recorded the conversation in its entirety!

Daniel wasn't sure what they were trying to achieve by this, but whatever it was, they only succeeded in stiffening his resolve by showing what kind of facile games they would resort to. Their weak mind games would not divert him from the path determined by *their* actions on and since 7/7, no matter what the consequences were.

A few days later Daniel sat hunched over the dining table.

His pen moved rapidly through a set of Criminal Injuries Compensation Authority application forms, ticking boxes and filling sections as the small amount of savings he was living on was dwindling.

A week later he retrieved a clutch of letters from his mailbox and tore open a white A4 envelope.

The response requested his medical reports and other documents to confirm with police and government departments that he was on the bus.

Then on January 27th 2006 he came home to find a small flashing light indicating a message had been left on his answer machine. He pressed a button and heard the voice of a man speaking in a Northern accent who identified himself as Detective Gary White of the Anti-Terrorist Branch.

The call concerned the investigation into the events of July 7th 2005 requesting his attendance to provide a *statement*.

Daniel pressed the repeat button and wrote down the mobile number the detective left. As he stared at the piece of paper, a thought crystallised in his mind.

For 7 months they had kept him out of the investigation, but this had become central to their cover-ups unravelling.

Daniel realised that it was the *belated act* of applying to the CICA for compensation that had begun the process of him *officially* being recorded as a passenger on the bus.

The flurry of correspondences and personal documents that landed on desks and in in-boxes confirmed his presence to the authorities and had begun a trail of evidence, a trail that lead back to *him*, the one eye-witness newspapers turned away; the one man who didn't buy the cover-up, who instead broke cover, refusing to be cowed by those trying to enforce it.

In the following weeks he broadened this documented response, applying to Mayor Livingstone's London Bombings Charitable Relief Fund.

He contacted the Independent Police Complaints Commission, with the aim of directing some heat back on Enfield Police Superintendent Simon O'Brien who the following month was swiftly transferred from Enfield borough to Haringey police.

Daniel also sent a letter to his local Member of Parliament - Joan Ryan MP for Enfield, detailing his treatment, keeping the bureaucratic juggernaut firmly on the road and casting the trial further and wider.

'To provide a statement' the message on his answer machine had said, as if the last 7 months were just a spooky figment of his imagination. Still, he had to get it over with, Daniel told himself, just like he'd told himself the day after the bombings.

Now being somewhat inexperienced when it came to the internal workings of a police station Daniel took a bus to Tottenham the next day to seek legal advice and hopefully a few re-assurances about his pending interview. A day later on January 29th he stood at the front desk of Edmonton Green police station in North London looking at the clock.

11:00am approached. He calculated it'd been six months, 3 weeks and 1 day since the bus bombing.

He wondered what line the detective's questioning might take, bearing in mind an army of investigators had concluded *their* investigations back in 2005.

They were only taking his statement at this stage to tidy up their paperwork, in case things were called into question at a later stage with regards to the IPCC complaint he was lodging. Once he'd begun his own paper trail this had had to be done.

It happened 10 days after he filled in the IPCC forms.

The 7 month time lapse meant that a group operating *inside* Peter Clarke's Anti-Terror Branch at Scotland Yard *must* have had a role in the cover-up of the 4th bomb.

11:00am came. Daniel pressed the buzzer on the counter.

He reminded himself to stay cautious, on-guard, but not *too* guarded, as these people were well versed in making unwary people incriminate themselves.

He saw a man making his way out of one the rooms behind the reinforced glass partition at the station's front.

The man exchanged words with a uniformed sergeant who nodded in the direction where Daniel stood with a stern look on his face, preparing himself for what was to come.

The man passed out of sight appearing moments later through a side door.

He approached with a business-like air.

'Ah, Daniel is it?' the man asked in an inquiring tone, sounding as if he was completely unaware of the identity of the man Intelligence officers and operatives had mounted an operation against for the last 7 months.

'Yes' came the curt reply.

His expression should have warded off any further attempt at faux introductions, but the detective still thrust out a hand offering a handshake.

Slightly raised eyebrows were all Daniel mustered, his hand's remained in his coat pockets causing the detective's unwelcome gesture to adapt, ushering him in the direction of the interview room.

On entering the small room Daniel's nostrils immediately scrunched up. It was a grey cubical with a table and two chairs. In the corner, fag ends littered the base of a fake tropical plant that doubled as an ashtray. Daniel sat down, trying to acclimatise to the thin stench of sweat that was overwhelmed by the heavy smell of cigarettes that hung in the air.

He eyed his soon to be interrogator, a balding white male in his mid-forties who's worn Reebok sweatshirt and faded blue trousers were reminiscent of a category of men he'd come across.

The detective checked the recording machine as Daniel placed a pad and pen on the biro scarred tabletop in readiness to take down a few notes of his own, about the detective, his surroundings and anything else of interest.

He reminded himself what his solicitor had said. It was just a statement. He wasn't being accused of anything.

Below the tabletop, beyond the detective's eye level Daniel's finger was poised over the record button of his mobile phone.

His hand came up covering his mouth as he coughed, covering the small beep his phone made as it began recording.

Introducing himself as Detective Gary White the man opened his pad and the interrogation began.

'This should have been done before, Daniel' the detective said. He sounded apologetic for the 7-month delay, attributing this *oversight* to a lack of resources available to follow up the calls to the anti-terrorist hotline.

Daniel nodded as though he understood, even though he knew plenty of survivors from the bus including a couple from Sydney, Australia called Tania Calabrese and her boyfriend Tony Cancellera had been interviewed the very same day.

The detective shuffled personal description forms, medical consent forms and a bus-seating plan that needed filling out.

'If we present you as a witness they'll want to know about these details' he said. Yeah right, thought Daniel. Seven months after the actual event took place and the *cover-up* had been concluded. It made perfect sense.

A timely witness statement from him would have turned the investigation upside-down or more precisely, identified those who were *really* responsible for the bus bombing.

'Daniel, here is a seating plan of the buses bottom deck.

Can you mark on it where you sat and say what you saw immediately after the bomb?'

Daniel studied it for a moment before placing crosses where the passengers on the lower deck had been.

'Wait... the seating layout is for a different model of bus!' Daniel said. The detective did not seem to feel this was too much of a problem and continued with his questioning.

'Think back... can you describe the three female survivors and what they did after the bomb?' the detective asked.

'Er... they just lay there' Daniel said, with a shrug.

'With a rising sense of fear' he added, sounding distant as he relived weird moment of silence after the explosion once more.

'A rising sense of fear? Good, very smart' the detective replied, sounding pleasantly charmed as he scribbled the words down.

'I'm glad you think so', Daniel replied.

'It's from a book I'm writing.'

The detective's scribbling stopped momentarily on hearing this. Daniel let out a faint yawn and leant back in his seat.

Not as smart as you say, but smarter than you think.

~Chapter 18~

The Interesting Narrative

Its release barely made a ripple amid the news items vying for coverage that week in May 2006. It had been quietly released to Members of Parliament in the House of Commons on May the 11th, finding it's way into the public domain days later.

Daniel downloaded a copy of the document from the BBC's website. The 41-page report was the British government's *narrative* account of the events of July 7th 2005.

It stated whom the investigating organisations, intelligence agencies and security services claimed were responsible for the bombings and suggested how the attacks were carried out.

So this was it. The *definitive* document the British government said replaced any need for any independent enquiry.

Daniel had awaited its release with more interest than most, having what could be described as more than just a passing interest in it's details. He printed a copy off and began reading intently, but by the time he reached the bottom of the sixth page he tossed it down on the couch beside him, knowing the report confirmed what he'd quietly suspected all along.

The report was generally vague, devoid of any solid factual evidence. Its coverage of the 4th bomb was restricted to details corroborating a theory put forward by a 61 year-old man calling himself Richard Jones.

His account received global media attention after 7/7 when he claimed to have been aboard the bus and seen the *bomber* dipping into a rucksack.

In another of his accounts he stated that it was *he* who told the bus driver to open the doors 70 meters from the actual bus stop so that he could get off moments before the bomb blast.

Jones said his reason for making this request was that he had become irritated after being jostled by a dark-skinned man he stood next to on the lower deck who kept dipping into his bag.

Daniel knew this was a lie because *he* had been the only male passenger on the lower deck when it was diverted to Tavistock Square.

Daniel went upstairs and returned with two newspapers.

He read an article from each paper and compared how the two accounts of Richard Jones evolved with the passage of time. The tabloid newspaper was dated Friday July the 8th.

It was Jones's initial account of the preceding day's events and in it the term he used to describe the suspect on the lower deck was *dark-skinned*.

In the second newspaper his story had changed. Jones had amended the description and location of the suspect he claimed to have seen. In his updated account in the second paper dated Monday July 11th the description changed to an *olive-skinned* person.

Daniel realised that this change had given the *suicide bomber theory* room for manoeuvre and it allowed someone who was not *dark-skinned* to be labelled the bus bomber.

Jones's amended version of events paved the way for the Government's narrative version of what happened, where it had shifted yet again, now categorically stating that the bomber's appearance was that of an *Asian* person.

The report went on to weave in the name of Hasib Hussain who was recorded on CCTV entering Kings Cross's main station through the Boot's chemists entrance after 9:00am.

10 minutes after the first 3 bombs were detonated.

The government's narrative then concluded that Hasib Hussain was a suicide bomber responsible for the bus bomb.

The 4th Bomb

Daniel noted down the government versions main claims.

<u>Report of the official account of the London bombings
in London on July 7th 2005</u>

09:00am:
*"Hussain walks out of King's Cross station through the chemist's
then enters WH Smith on the station concourse and buys a 9v
battery. It is possible that a new battery was needed to detonate the
device, but this is only speculation at this point"*

Page 5, Paragraph 6.

09:19am:
*"A man fitting Hasib Hussain's description was seen on the lower
deck earlier, fiddling repeatedly with his rucksack"*

Page 6, Paragraph 1.

09:47am:
*"The bomb goes off, killing 14 people including Hussain.
But we have no further evidence at this stage."*

Page 6, Paragraph 2.

The report elaborated on the Jones's story that initially fuelled
speculation that the bus was destroyed by a suicide bomber.
The first glaring error Daniel saw in the report was the time it
said the bus left Euston. Daniel knew it left at 09:31am *not*
09:19am as they claimed on page 6, he had checked the time
and tried to call his office. He knew Jones was never on the
lower deck of the bus where he'd initially claimed he was.
Now the report said a man *fitting* Hasib Hussain's description
was seen on the lower deck by him *earlier*.
It had been carefully worded to shift Jones's fictitious sighting
from the lower to the upper-deck, where it was well
established the bomb had been detonated.

209

Daniel ruminated. Interestingly, the claims the report made had opened up a few new lines of enquiry.

Just knowing Richard Jones was never on the upper deck wasn't enough, he needed proof.

Where was Jones going that morning? What was his purpose? Daniel could only wonder, but the official report and Jones's previous claims all pointed to one fact. It pointed to the fact that Jones had *rehearsed* his original account *before* the bus blast took place.

Jones's inconsistencies started because he was given access to the media at such an early stage, well before all the bodies from the bus were properly identified.

Details surrounding the iconic image of the bombed bus were rapidly beamed worldwide along with his first false account. Only afterwards did those in charge of the cover-up, realise their error and began changing the story.

Future versions incorporated his nonsensical reason explaining why the bus driver stopped 70 metres away from the only bus stop on Tavistock Square and why only the driver only opened the bus's centre exit doors, allowing some passengers and the *real* bomber to get off but none of the pedestrians trying to board, to board.

Just looking at the ambiguous language used in the government report Daniel sensed much was yet to emerge.

If Richard Jones's account was a bungled media plant he had to prove it somehow.

It might be easier to prove Hasib Hussain didn't kill those bus passengers that day, he thought, trying to approach the problem from a different angle.

Why was the 4th bomb delayed almost an hour after the first three? He was sure there was a connection there.

The answer was rattling around in his head somewhere.

He knew it. He just had to make sense of it somehow, then the facts would be within reach.

Daniel rummaged through the newspapers, notes and articles he kept in a box at the bottom of his wardrobe.

He pulled out a DVD and returned to the next room, sticking it in the DVD player. With a wave of the remote control he summoned up yet another rerun of a 7/7 documentary.

He'd struck upon an idea.

The key to disproving the *suicide bomber* theory Jones helped propagate was the bomb explosion itself.

Did Hussian detonate it using a 9-volt battery as claimed in the government's narrative version or was it detonated by some other means?

He rewound it to the part of the documentary in question, pressed play and watched John Falding's video account of that fateful morning again.

Falding's girlfriend Anat Rosenberg had dashed out of the front door already late for work.

After she'd left her boyfriend's flat he turned on the television and watched a news channel. After sometime, sketchy reports of explosions flashed across the screen. Falding relayed the details of his last conversation with her to the interviewer.

'She'd been trying to get through for the last half hour. There was a problem, on the tube... an emergency of some sort. She said she was taking a bus.
About 20 minutes later at 9.45am my phone rang for a second time that morning. It was Anat again, updating me on her situation.'
Yes, there had been an incident at Liverpool Street and Edgware Road, I told her. And then I heard a scream in the background'
Falding's voice faltered.
'It was like nothing I've ever heard before. It was ghastly.
The phone line went dead... it was horrible.'

'Wait!' Daniel gasped, almost disbelieving his ears.

He hit rewind then pressed play again.

It was precisely what he'd been looking for.

Falding's account corresponded with what Daniel saw on the bus moments before the blast.

The brunette seated right at the back by the window had her mobile phone clasped against her ear.

In the documentary Falding said she called him at 09:45 and they were still talking when the bomb exploded minutes later.

Anat Rosenburg was the *only* passenger to die on the bus's lower deck. 09.45am was 15 minutes after Daniel had given up trying to contact his office to tell them he'd be late, just before the bus pulled out of Euston bus terminus.

Daniel thumbed through his box of newspaper clippings hoping to find something corroborating the mobile networks' status that day.

He searched through his stack of papers and came across a police statement explaining why they were initially called power surges. It went on to say that mobile network coverage had been switched off to prevent the possible detonation of explosives by mobile signal. This explained the long queues formed at phone kiosks that morning as commuters evacuated at Euston found their calls couldn't get through. Falding's emotional account had proved why the bus had been held up!

The two dark cars held-up the bus, *then* they diverted it once they'd received the signal that the mobile networks were switched back on. This enabled the bomb to be detonated *remotely* using a phone signal and it allowed Anat's last call.

The actions of the two dark cars led to the destruction of the bus and also destroyed the theory that Hasib Hussain was the bomber, because no suicide bomber detonates the explosives they have strapped about their person using a mobile phone signal. They would simply pull a *cord*.

And how did the operatives in the two cars know that an explosive device was on the bus? Because *they* were part of the team that planted it, they being none other than MI5, British Intelligence.

Furthermore, Daniel knew he had seen the man who planted the bomb. The bomber had seen him too.

The bomber was the white male in his mid-twenties with brown hair, wearing a grey two-tone shower-proof top he saw dart off the bus just before the driver shut the doors.

Daniel remembered how he came down from the upper deck when the driver stopped the bus 70 metres away from the bus stop, but instead of disembarking like others who realised King's Cross was a 10 minute walk away he sat beside the exit doors exchanging surreptitious glances.

Then the man sprang out of his seat and darted off the bus just before the doors shut. He planted the bomb on the upper deck. He was the bomber, and was the last person to get off before the bus crawled to its final destination.

Daniel cast his mind back to that morning.

With crystal clarity and strangely numbed emotions he'd observed what was happening around him. In a twinkling of an eye it unfolded before him and now it was unravelling in front of him.The men that rushed forward carrying out roles in a detached manner with workman like efficiency.

The two dark cars shortly before. The cameraman in black in the immediate aftermath. The triage, ready and waiting on the grass of Tavistock green that looked suspiciously like part of the terror drills Peter Power spoke of. Then there was the man in grey, wailing on the ground feigning injury 50 metres away from the bus, complete with a bandage around his head and a neatly torn trouser leg. A terror rehearsal gone awry?

Or a planned terror attack? It all looked so staged, like a setup.

Daniel's mind returned to the BBC radio interview of Peter Power talking about the terror drills taking place on the same day at the same locations. It had seemed a blatant attempt at deception at the time, but the whole preplanned-ness of the bloody slaughter of innocents near the site of The Tavistock Institute now rang true.

What had begun as deep misgivings about the accuracy of news reports explaining how Christian met his death had gathered momentum and led to this.

Now Daniel stood on the brink of knowing the full truth.

~Chapter 19~

Richard Jones - Live At The Terror Drill

As it had done in the wake of the 911 attacks in the U.S, a spew of websites sprung up around the July 7th attacks in London. Almost all of the early sites were borne of a stunned populaces unified stance against terror. Then, as the investigation became entangled in a web of contradictory accounts, discussions on these forums became more quizzical as more pointed questions began to be asked and inconsistencies highlighted.

The swift rise in this questioning was spurred on by the Blair government's refusal to hold an enquiry into the bombings.

This flagrant disregard for democratic procedure fuelled a growing discontentment with the total lack of factual evidence and the eventual release of the government's version failed to allay any of these fears.

Comparisons were already being made with Blair's dodgy dossier that took the British armed services into Iraq on a lie.

Segments of Daniel's Tavistock Square thread on the Ligali forum had found it's way onto some 7/7 discussion forums.

He followed the responses to his account with interest and was amused by some of the rabid retorts dismissing his account as the rants of a heretic and a fantasist, while others cautiously embraced it, just hoping it wasn't too good to be true. Contributions from truth-seekers and conspiracy theorists ranged from the plausible and helpful to the faintly ridiculous.

Many forum contributors appeared to be genuinely disgruntled with the way the British government had ridden roughshod over public opinion, so learning the stark truth made many of them feel uneasy realising what their own government had done to their people.

A lot were long-time placard-wavers who did the state a favour by attending marches, giving the outside world the impression that by allowing and totally ignoring their protests, Britain was a shining beacon of democracy. The funny thing is, in the back of their mind they probably hoped Britain still was. It never had been. He viewed the sullen stare of the man he'd seen with a bandage around his head 25 seconds after the explosion.

His sighting of him in Tavistock Square was being called into question on a 7/7 forum's thread he was reading. New footage showing the bandaged man being led away by two intelligence operatives near Russell Square tube station. He was being led away from the location the Piccadilly line survivors were evacuated to. It was also the *exact* same location of one of Peter Power's terror drills that had taken place earlier that morning at 8.20am, thirty minutes before the first three blasts.

The question was asked. How could this Daniel character claim to have seen the bandaged man in Tavistock Square seconds after the bus bomb? Was he a C.I.A plant? Another concluded he was a religious nut after concatenating Daniel and 7/7.

But Daniel knew exactly what he'd seen. The man's head bandage and neatly ripped trouser leg were major things that caused his serious misgivings seconds after the explosion and led to him returning to the square to take a second look.

Luckily a contributor was able to confirm the image Daniel recognised the bandaged man in was actually taken down the road from Russell Square at the location of the evacuation and Peter Power's Terror drill in a place called Brundswick Square.

This, she said, was confirmed this by the little yellow tag on his wrist denoting his injury's priority level of 2.

She knew this because she herself had been evacuated from the Piccadilly line tube that morning.

Her name was Rachel North.

She had provided Daniel with what he'd been waiting for.

It was the reason he'd highlighted the bandaged man in the first place, hoping someone out there could shed light on how he'd got bandaged so quickly.

This new piece of information confirming his injury priority made the bandaged man's behaviour all the more curious.

If he wasn't in an ambulance it meant his priority tag had been ignored for some reason. Was it because his injuries were *fake* or was he just there for the cameras? If he *was* part of Peter Power's terror drills it explained his mock injuries and subsequent reappearance at the site of another *terror drill* not long after in Tavistock Square that became the real thing!

A few hours spent sifting the Internet came up with the answer Daniel was looking for. He found a foreign website with unedited rushes of the scene at Brunswick Square, the site of the Russell Square evacuation and earlier terror drill.

Daniel couldn't understand the language the voice-over was in, it sounded Scandinavian but the footage clearly showed same the bandaged man he had seen lying on the pavement in Tavistock Square. It focused in on his face as he was hauled to his feet by two operatives with rucksacks who'd been standing over him. It showed them taking him in the direction of Tavistock Square. Further footage of evacuees from Russell Square showed another survivor speaking of the number of Hail Mary's said and utter panic in the 30 minute period they spent waiting for the electricity to be turned of to allow transport staff to arrive and escort them to safety.

Then the footage cut to a survivor from the Russell Square explosion at 08.51am giving a press interview 30 to 40 minutes after the blast. Clasping a bottle of Evian water in one hand she wiped tears from her cheek with the back of the other, tears smudged the black soot from the tunnel down her face as she gave the ITN news crew an emotional account of the horror she'd seen as they were led to safety.

Daniel replayed the footage a few more times then compared the unedited Scandinavian footage with the clip broadcast by the British media. A sizable amount missing from the British version and he knew why.

He clicked on the media player and viewed the Scandinavian clip full screen. As he sat back watching it he saw a face in the background. It seemed familiar. Very familiar.

Hardly able to believe he eyes, Daniel gasped. There, strolling leisurely behind the tearful lady being interviewed was none other than *Richard Jones*. Daniel rubbed his eyes.

It was him, Richard Jones, as clear as day. His distinctive grey head of hair and facial features were totally recognisable.

Daniel compared Jones's picture with a headshot from an online article and could hardly believe it. Jones was even wearing the *same* pale pink shirt in both pictures. They were taken on the same day!

This was it! The proof he needed. It proved that the man whose account was responsible for starting the suicide bomber theory later relied upon in the government narrative was a *false witness*!

The man who framed Hasib Hussain could *never* have made it to Euston in time to catch the bus because it left at 9:31am and here he was, captured, *on film* over a mile away at the exact *same* time. The proof was the time of the female Piccadilly line bomb evacuee's interview.

~Chapter 20~

The New Nation

On a warm afternoon late in June 2006 Daniel stood on a busy high road waiting for Richard.

To anyone passing he appeared relaxed in a white t-shirt, a baseball cap, khaki quarter length shorts and Reebok sports sandals, but inwardly he remained vigilant.

It had been 3 months since he moved out of his apartment, away from the scrutiny of Enfield, North London to the comparatively sedate streets of South London.

Though he couldn't be 100% certain he wasn't being followed, he felt more at ease. Even if he was, the surveillance had receded to a more covert level, a level that didn't send his eyes darting between innocuous strangers.

Of course tracking via the signal his mobile phone emitted, eavesdropped phone conversations and emails remained a point of consideration, but that was something he could live with, as most handsets gave off a signal pinpointing the owners location to their network provider.

Anyone monitoring Daniel presently would have found him in the heart of London's Bangladeshi community, near Aldgate, an area where 70% of the population was Muslim. It was a part of London that over the centuries had been home to waves of Jewish immigration and French Huguenots before them, but now mostly Asian businesses were situated in the doorways off the Commercial Road; the main eastern artery into the City.

A gold chain dangled from the neck of a skinny Asian youth in a black t-shirt and white Reeboks eyeing him from nearby.

The youth stood with a hand in the back pocket of his designer jeans regarding Daniel with suspicion as he leant against railings outside Aldgate East underground station.

Daniel was more concerned with avoiding the glare of the many CCTV cameras lining the congested route into the city than that of the youth's. Perhaps his stance was in response to the ongoing media onslaught causing young Asians to mistrust anyone from outside their community.

The British media was busy turning mainstream society against Muslims by creating tensions and divisions as its anti-Islamic agenda cranked into gear with the first anniversary of the 7/7 bombings looming.

Asians had more reason to be wary of accusing stares, half-heard whispers or becoming the victims of police stop and searches. In recent weeks two Asian families had their houses raided, were hauled off for questioning and held in custody for weeks without any evidence or any charges.

Daniel looked over at the youth and shrugged. He could empathise to some extent. It was similar to the cycle of demonisation and discrimination members of the African community had routinely endured since the 1970's.

From his back pocket Daniel took out four Pay-As-You-Go SIM cards and inserted one bearing Richard's initials into his small Nokia phone. The Nokia was the cheapest, most basic handset on the market. It was so cheap it had no back-up cell, meaning it was truly network *invisible* when turned off.

It was switched it on before making calls and turned it off as soon as the call ended, ensuring it could not be easily tracked.

Most mobiles have a back-up cell, meaning they still emit a small network signal even when switched off. If a phones battery is removed then replaced and it retained the time and date information it proves that the phone was always visible by its network and is thus, trackable.

The downside was that Daniel had to set the time and date each time it was switched it on, but this he could live with.

His large fingers were still fiddling with its finicky keys when he recognised a figure, verging on the portly, emerging from the underground with a portfolio under his arm.

'Apologies... how've you been?' said Richard, nodding his head resolutely while giving him a firm handshake.

'Good thanks' piped Daniel, whose casual demeanor didn't quite reflect the level of concern the query posed.'

'Shall we? Richard offered, glancing cautiously in one direction while gesturing in the other and he led the way.

Daniel upped his pace to keep up with Richard's brisk pace.

'Angela's been held up on another story I'm afraid.'

Daniel raised an eyebrow, would the day he'd been building up to be a no-show?

'She'll be back in the office around two thirty' Richard added.

Phew, Daniel thought, relieved. For him today was all about being relaxed so the interview could be conducted in a calm manner, he'd told himself.

'Let's grab a coffee. We'll go through what you'll talk about'

'Fine' nodded Daniel.

'Did you bring the information you mentioned?'

'Yeah it's all here, in this document I prepared' assured Daniel.

'*The Missing Minutes,* it lists precisely what happened between 09:19am when the government's narrative ends and 09:47am when the bomb exploded aboard the bus.

They entered an Italian-style deli on Commercial Road a short walk from where the newspaper's offices were located.

Daniel sat at a table with his back to the door. Richard went up to the counter and returned placing two cappuccinos and a toasted paninni on the table.

'Thanks' Daniel said, inspecting the sandwich's filling before taking a bite. He recognised the look on Richard's face.

His usual joviality and easy laugh were not in evidence.

He seemed a lot more cautious than when he'd liberally name-dropped a few well-placed media contacts over coffee in Starbucks a couple of weeks back.

The small seed of knowledge Daniel had planted had obviously taken on larger proportions since their last meeting.

Just as shock and awe is replaced by fear and doubt, the wide-eyed wonderment in Richard's eyes at the conclusion of their second meeting had been replaced with a definite edginess; a process Daniel knew the paper's readership and the British public would go through at some stage.

Its symptoms were highlighted when an Asian man walked into the shop. Richard's eyes flitted towards the door as he entered. His conversation halted as the young man passed where they sat. He turned tentatively in his seat to see the man sitting at the rear of the deli, tapping on the table as if waiting for someone or something.

Richard turned back around, leant forward towards Daniel and continued explaining the process in a lowered tone.

Daniel finished his sandwich and elaborated on his overall strategy.

'The idea is to do this article which then stokes interest in one of the larger broadsheets like The Guardian or The Independent, to do an exclusive'.

'Take a look', he said, passing Richard the document.

Richard studied it carefully, nodding morosely every so often. It outlined the pertinent facts that were missed and the major discrepancies in the government's narrative version of events.

Watchful of the time Richard checked his watch again and the two of them left the deli for The New Nation's offices a few doors away.

The receptionist took them to a meeting room on the 3rd floor. Through its partially open blinds Daniel looked out over a car park. He declined the receptionist's offer of tea or coffee and sat down. Here goes nothing he thought.

Richard sat drumming his fingers on the table. His mood seemed to have lightened in more familiar surroundings and lit up further when a woman entered the room.

'Hi, how've you been?' she said beaming at Daniel while addressing Richard.

'Fine' Richard replied, he stood up and introduced Daniel to Angela Foster, who apologised for the hasty re-scheduling.

'Pleased to meet you Daniel' she said as he leant forward to shake her hand. At once her warm smile put him at ease, though her bright air made him wonder if she would really be able to grasp the *full* magnitude of his story.

State Terror, Government Lies And Murder did not make for a bright and breezy headline. He reminded himself to stick to his strategy. Don't fall into the trap many whistleblowers fell into, releasing *all* they knew in one go. It was something he'd read in an article penned by a certain Eliza Manningham-Buller, head of MI5 a while back. Richard looked across the table at him. Daniel could tell Richard had the feeling there were a few things he hadn't told him. He was right, but it was complicated and there was a plan to stick to. The British Intelligence operatives had whitewashed him out of the picture ever since July 7th, so first he had to establish the fact that he *was* on the bus. Only when that had been achieved could he begin exposing the pack of lies in the Jones account and the government's narrative version. He glanced at Richard.

A smile had returned to his face. He was leaning back in his chair looking pleased with himself. This was only the first stage, Daniel told himself, smiling across at Angela. She laid a notepad and pens out on the table, switched the tape recorder in the middle of the table on and the interview began.

As he left the building after finishing the interview Daniel did a small piece of mental arithmetic. Ten days.

It was ten days till the article's publication.

On some days the imagined ramifications of what he was doing threatened his still moments, but for each of those ten days he walked along an astounding threshold where the everyday and mundane were interchangeable with the fantastic and inconceivable.

They had used the cloak of secrecy to cover their cowardly acts and evil murderous deeds. That was why he'd chosen the glare of publicity to expose the truth to send them scuttling back into the dark shadows from whence they came.

Each day counted down to the launch of something that might prove more explosive than any bomb planted that day, to a day affecting British history and its role in the world order forever. There was no going back for him or them.

Those with a lust for power had taken that fateful decision and now they would feel what true power is.

They feared the truth and would do everything in their power to control it or conceal it, but as Daniel had been reminded by a Jamaican man he sat alongside in the waiting area of the Independent Police Complaints building in Holborn, *the truth will set you free*.

When Monday came, the day the paper landed in newsagents Daniel spent most of the day trying to fill his head with anything but the article. It seemed taking the final step filled him with questions. One question he asked was what he would do if it wasn't published? He'd lain awake fretting over recent nights after coming across an image of the photographer who took his photo for the newspaper on the Internet. In it the photographer was dressed in a white PVC suit pictured taking snaps alongside police forensics officers of the aftermath in Tavistock Square.

Daniel knew he was close to achieving his first objective, but knew disappointment was something he still had to be prepared for.

What if the printing presses had been halted by a group of snarling operatives, menacing the staff with veiled threats?

What if Angela's story had been pulled or the newspaper muzzled by the intervention of a little known government department with far reaching powers?

His walk the following day across Brixton's bustling high road to Acre Lane felt oddly mundane for what supposedly was such a pivotal moment.

He threw a small wave to the man tending the baseball cap and cheap sunglasses stall outside the Internet café.

The vendors smiling eyes returned a nod in return, just another regular face he recognised, entering to face a moment of truth. There, on the newspaper stand was the answer to all of his questioning, *The New Nation*.

Daniel stooped down and recognised his image.

He'd made the front cover!

'ONE YEAR ON' read its caption, his heart fluttered as he turned the page. He inhaled deeply, as deeply as he'd done a second before he'd taken flight from the wreckage of the bombed bus a year before.

What began as a search to understand the truth behind what he witnessed had crept over a tiny threshold and was now set to turn bigger wheels in motion. He stood gazing at the front page, amazing. The date was 4th of July, a day in history when the peoples of a fledgling nation stood up against British tyranny. Glancing over his shoulder he saw web surfers huddled over a row of monitors. Outside the street seemed clear of observers. The stallholder remained at his spot.

Daniel felt himself brim with an inner joy.

All he'd endured over the past 12 months had amounted to this small step. He could've punched the air, but showed no outward sign of emotion as joy cannot be celebrated unless it is shared with others and this was only the beginning.

He wouldn't let it become yesterday's news. Now the next stage could begin. Releasing facts to a public who'd been fed a diet of thwarted terror plots from one of the 2000 Jihad cells the government claimed were at large.

Tumultuous times certainly lay ahead, but it was all part of the process. Evil could no longer hide. The new horizon had dawned. A new age of clarity was shining down on us all.

Evil would be consumed by the fear of it's own making.

Daniel smiled. He'd snared the cowardly spooks and their leaders who think all that is hidden remains unknown.

Now the truth was there for anyone who sought it, because in the light of the truth everything becomes apparent.

He paid for a drink he took from the chiller cabinet and a copy of The New Nation then stepped outside. As it had done a year before and on countless occasions since, the bright sunshine reminded him of the day his journey to work was interrupted when reality burst upon him. The resigned sigh he gave the moment the blast sent his life flashing before him had seemed an odd reaction at the time. Maybe it was in recognition of a new journey; a new beginning, perhaps. Maybe he'd actually arrived at work? Or had work arrived at him?

'Bloody shirt!' Daniel chuckled to himself, thinking back to the ironing that made him catch the late train.

From that moment he'd known it was going to be one of those days, a day in which you take a deep breath and try to deal with whatever comes your way, steadfastly continuing on towards your destination.

~Epilogue ~

So there you have it, the whole truth surrounding the 4th bomb and the terror attacks on London. It's the story of what happened after I ran and how the strange things I'd seen compelled me to return to the scene of carnage minutes later.

My reaction and response that morning may be deemed unusual, but it is in moments of truth that we truly act *instinctively*, reacting without the constraints of learned responses. I use the term *instinctively* loosely; I could mean inspirationally, meaning what drives us as beings, something that comes from deep within the spirit or soul.

Life taught me to never accept anything on face value alone, so of course my first response that day was to question what I'd seen and far too many things did not add up.

'From facts we glean the truth.' I seem to remember a western philosopher said words along these lines and I wanted facts.

The public wanted facts. These *wants* culminated in the publication of this book based on notes I began scribbling down as soon as I got home that day. It began as an outpouring, such was the burden of what I'd witnessed.

My later experiences at the hands of Special Reconnaissance Regiment operatives and other elements of British Intelligence added to them and gave me further insight into the neuroses of those acting at the behest of the British government.

As for me… whatever happens *happens*.

This process has proven something that has remained with me. That we have entered an age of clarity.

We are more powerful than *they* would have us believe.

Many already see through those who crave and cling to power. They see through the politicians and those performing feeble conjuring tricks before our eyes in a vain bid to take the real power that belongs to us all, *the people*.

For the diligent truth-seekers out there, your probing questions and constructive criticism was appreciated assisting greatly in the course of researching and writing of this book. So to you all I say keep searching and spreading the word!

The 3rd bomb on the Piccadilly line train left some odd clues. Maybe one day someone will come forward with a vital piece of evidence to expose those responsible, sending another signal to the British government that we will not be ruled by lies and governed by fear, not here or overseas.

My voice is just one of many guarding against this, so the masses may know what is afoot and remain vigilant as the truth is the only thing preventing Britain's complete descent into fascism.

It seems to me that the truth is fast becoming a luxury; known or *owned* by a privileged few or power crazed elite, no longer something underpinning any democratic society's core values.

I say this because I think I can just about remember the last *truth* I heard spoken on the British governments behalf.

It was on July 7th 2005, when I sat aboard a tube and a message issued from the P.A system saying there was a 'power surge'.

A power surge indeed.

Daniel Obachike

Every person in this book is an actual person. Every event in this book accurately depicts precisely what happened in the exact location or establishment in which it took place.